'Lean Healthcare'
Improving the patient's experience

David Fillingham

Kingsham Press

www.akdpress.com

First published in 2008
by Kingsham Press

Oldbury Complex
Marsh Lane
Easthampnett
Chichester, West Sussex
PO18 0JW
United Kingdom

Typeset in Minion

Printed and bound in the UK by Biddles Ltd., Kings Lynn, Norfolk

ISBN: 978-1-904235-56-9

British Library Cataloging in Publication Data
A catalogue record of this book is available from the British Library

Fillingham, David

Contents

About the author

David Fillingham CBE has been Chief Executive at Bolton Hospitals NHS Trust since September 2004. He joined the NHS in 1989 having previously worked in personnel management and marketing positions with Pilkington plc. After a short period at Mersey Regional Health Authority, David has occupied a number of Chief Executive positions – in Primary Care at Wirral FHSA from 1991 until 1993; in commissioning at St Helens & Knowsley HA from 1993 until 1997; and in acute hospital services at North Staffordshire Hospitals Trust from 1997 to 2001.

From 2001 to 2004, David was Director of the NHS Modernisation Agency responsible for developing new ways of working and promoting leadership development across the NHS as a whole. David is now relishing the challenge of putting that national experience into practice back on the frontline of the NHS at Bolton. In particular he is deeply involved in applying 'lean' principles to healthcare.

David lives in St Helens in Lancashire. Other than the NHS, his passions are watching his local rugby league team and spending time with his wife and two daughters.

Acknowledgements

This book would not have existed without the work of Bolton Hospitals 3,500 staff. To a large extent it is their story. I am deeply indebted to them for their commitment, compassion and their willingness to try out this wacky new idea called 'lean'.

On a personal basis a number of individuals have provided me with tremendous advice and support, both in adapting lean for healthcare and in writing this account of it.

Dan Jones and his colleagues at the Lean Enterprise Academy have been unfailingly generous in offering advice, guidance and encouragement. Alan Mitchell provided helpful comments on the book's structure and on early drafts.

Our Consulting partners, Simpler, have patiently taught us the fundamentals of the lean approach. Along the way they seem to have been infected by our own enthusiasm for improving the NHS. Particular thanks must go to Nick Middleton and Chris Cooper who got us started on the journey and to Chris Lloyd, John Rutter and Martin Bartolf for their support and guidance.

A number of other lean experts have provided me with a range of differing and stimulating perspectives including Jim Womack, Michael Ballé, John Drew and George Koenigsaecker.

My early grounding in healthcare quality improvement took place before I came to Bolton. I am grateful to the staff of the former NHS Modernisation Agency for all that I learned from them and also to Don Berwick and his colleagues at IHI for their wisdom and inspiration.

Some of the World's leading lean healthcare pioneers have been a great inspiration to us. It was hearing John Toussaint, the Chief Executive Officer of Thedacare in Wisconin, USA, speak about his own hospital's achievements that really got me started on my own lean journey. I am grateful to John for his advice and the generous support which his organisation has provided to us.

Similarly David Ben-Tovim and his colleagues at Flinders Hospital in Adelaide, South Australia, have proved an inspirational example, as has Mike Rona and the team at Virginia Mason, Seattle.

I owe a great debt of gratitude to Rebecca Bridge who produced the manuscript for this book with immense professionalism and patience.

Finally, I want to acknowledge the contribution of those closest to me. My wife Janet has been an unfailing source of wise advice and encouragement. Without her this book would never have got started, let alone finished … thank you. A big thank you also to my two daughters, Sarah and Anna. Not only have this book and Bolton's lean journey meant that I have had less time to spend with them, but they have had to put up with my becoming a lean obsessive at the same time.

A shorter account of this story was first published in the *Journal of Leadership in Health Services* (2007), Vol 20, Issue 4 under the title of 'Can lean save lives?'.

Foreword

Daniel T. Jones

Chairman, *Lean Enterprise Academy*, UK – http://www.leanuk.org – and co-author
of *The Machine that Changed the World, Lean Thinking* and *Lean Solutions*

This book tells the story of the one of the pioneering experiments to demonstrate that
the lean thinking principles developed many years ago by Toyota can deliver equally
impressive improvements in healthcare. I first met David when he was Chief Executive
of the Modernisation Agency, set up by the National Health Service to develop and
spread new thinking in hospitals across the UK. During my visit I learnt about the very
interesting work they had been doing with lean.

Over a cup of coffee at a Lean Summit in the USA later that year I asked David what
he and his staff were planning to do next and how these early experiments could in some
way be preserved and built upon. In typical fashion David said that after telling others
about lean he was now going to do it himself, as Chief Executive of Bolton Hospitals
NHS Trust. I could tell he was deadly serious and this would be the one of the first
experiments that would turn lean from just another improvement tool to the management system that would transform healthcare over the next decade.

That meeting was one of the triggers that convinced me that healthcare was now
ready for lean, not just in the UK but around the world. David readily agreed to help me
set up the UK *Lean Healthcare Network* to increase awareness of lean and bring together
early pioneers struggling to convince their colleagues of the potential of lean. Within
two years awareness is widespread and many other hospitals have begun to follow
David's lead. Confirmation that this is a global phenomenon came when we organised
the truly memorable first *Global Lean Healthcare Summit* in 2007.

During many visits to Bolton I have always been impressed by David's enthusiasm
and his ability to see the bigger picture of what was possible with lean. He and his staff
have also been very generous in sharing their early struggles with others and he always
rightly stresses that they have just begun their lean journey and there is so much more
to be discovered. We all learnt a lot from his early example. What began as a series of
rapid improvement events quickly became a framework for seeing the hospital as a collection of processes through which patients, staff, records, tests, supplies and many other
things wandered from department to department with many delays and queues.

This book tells the beginning of the lean journey at Bolton. It should be an inspiration to others to follow their example. There is as yet no one best way to go lean in
healthcare and others are conducting different experiments in hospitals across the

world. Learning from all these pioneering experiments will be a fascinating and very rewarding journey in the next decade and one that will I am convinced make a big contribution to improving the care of patients in the future.

Goodrich, April 2008

Chapter One

Introduction

SUMMARY

- When compared to many other sectors, Healthcare is at best seriously under-performing; at worst it is a failing industry;

- Across the world, healthcare systems are serving their customers poorly, have many demoralised staff, and are providing their funders with poor value for money;

- Valiant efforts have been made to improve in many countries; there have been some successes but these have been marginal rather than transformational;

- Lean methodologies have revolutionised quality, profitability and staff morale in many businesses in widely differing sectors outside of healthcare;

- There is a growing body of evidence that lean can work in healthcare and deliver the same level of transformational improvement.

A true story

I know that everyone gets highs and lows during their average working day. This is certainly true of hospital Chief Executives such as myself. I recently experienced both within the space of an hour. The high came when I encountered one of our patients as I was walking through the hospital. I knew her slightly from a business function I had been at and so she knew what job I did. She stopped me to say 'Mr Fillingham, can I just have a word with you about the care I have received at your hospital'. Your heart does tend to sink sometimes when patients stop you and say this! On this occasion I needn't have worried. This lady had a chronic condition which meant she was a frequent visitor to the hospital, both as an outpatient and sometimes for an inpatient stay as well. She had nothing but praise for the treatment she had received.

She recounted how every member of staff she met was unfailingly friendly and polite. She felt treated as an individual – for example one of the nurses remembered the names of her children and always asked about them. Her condition was quite a rare one but the hospital had carried out all the appropriate tests and made a quick diagnosis which meant that she was now on the best treatment available. She rarely had to wait long for appointments or for special tests or treatment. On the few occasions when she had been admitted as an inpatient, everything had gone smoothly.

She felt that the wards were clean and well organized, that the staff were busy but went out of their way to make time for those patients who needed a bit of extra special attention. She even complimented us on the food which she said was better than most of the hotels she had stayed in! She said she wanted me to know these things as she was sure I often got complaints rather than praise. She hoped that I would pass on her personal thanks to all the staff for how hard they worked. I walked away down the corridor feeling a glow of pride. It seemed we were getting some things right after all.

I got back to my office to find the usual full inbox on my email and a pile of papers awaiting signature. The pile of papers contained the low point of my day. It took the form of a passionate and strongly worded letter. It came from the daughter of a patient who had sadly died in our hospital. Her daughter had visited her every day of her six week stay, and almost everything that could have gone wrong did.

She spent time on three different wards and the high dependency unit. Some of her moves were not well planned and on one occasion her family didn't even know that she had switched wards. Despite lots of different doctors being involved, we struggled to diagnose her condition and her family was never confident that she was receiving the best treatment that she could have had.

Whilst two of the wards that she stayed on were felt to be acceptable, the daughter was adamant that the care on two of the other wards, to quote her, 'fell way below what should have been expected in a civilized country'. These wards seemed to be chaotic. They were cluttered and untidy. The nurses and doctors were too busy and harassed to pay proper attention to patients or to talk to the relatives which meant that they always felt helpless and didn't know what was going on.

Because the family were there and asked lots of questions they got the sense that they were being regarded as trouble makers. The daughter said that they saw their mum fade away before their very eyes. Whilst the family felt that it was probably true that their mum's time had come and that no hospital could have saved her, the distressing last weeks of her life were memories that would stay with them forever. None of the family wanted to use the Hospital's services again.

The contrast between these two experiences couldn't be more marked, yet they happened in the same hospital and I heard about both of them within the space of an hour. It would be easy to pretend that the second case was a one-off, a regrettable slip in our standards. But I am sure that anyone who has been a patient or a relative of someone in hospital will know that unfortunately it wasn't an isolated incident.

All hospitals suffer from these problems, not just mine. The almost daily debate in English newspapers about the state of the NHS provides ample evidence for this. Indeed international studies reveal that this is a world wide problem.

The challenge for everyone working healthcare is to work out how we can get more of the first kind of experience and fewer of the second. I'll go further than that: how can we make it so that patients **only** receive the first kind of experience – that we deliver best possible care for every single patient every single time? This book is an exploration of whether a 'lean' approach – so successfully used in manufacturing and some service industries – can deliver this ambitious goal for healthcare. Can lean save the NHS?

The beginnings of my own lean journey

From 2001–2004, I was the Director of the NHS Modernisation Agency. The Agency was responsible for spreading quality improvement approaches throughout the whole of the NHS. Although it was relatively short-lived, it provided training in quality tools and techniques to over 100,000 NHS staff and supported many notable achievements including the transformation of care in emergency departments and significant reductions in waiting times for cancer treatment and coronary heart disease.

In this job, I was exposed to many different approaches to healthcare improvement. I saw at first hand some significant successes as well as initiatives which headed off up blind alleys. But despite the successes of the NHS during this period they were almost always programmatic. By this I mean that there were pockets of improvement for particular services, orthopaedics, coronary heart disease, emergency departments for example. It was rare for any hospital, let alone an entire healthcare system, to apply a systematic approach to quality improvement across the whole of its activity.

I returned to the NHS as Chief Executive of Bolton Hospital in September 2004 and began the search for a way in which I could put in to practice what I had learned at the Modernisation Agency. In my first few months in Bolton, I spent many hours talking to business leaders outside of healthcare as well as discussing approaches to quality improvement with those managers and clinical leaders who had made the most progress in reducing harm and improving quality for their patients.

By July 2005, I had become convinced that we needed something different to anything that had been tried before. All too often quality improvement was regarded as something best left to a few maverick enthusiasts. It was the province of those who could talk with authority about capacity and demand management, or statistical process control charts. These were seen as people who were more interested in tools and techniques than in the day-to-day realities of managing health services and providing care. If we were to achieve a whole scale transformation, then this simply couldn't be right. What was required was an over-arching philosophy that would engage everyone.

We needed an approach which was not just about the technical aspects of quality improvement but which would blend these with the disciplines of organisational development and clinical governance. In short, we needed to put the improvement of quality and safety at the heart of all that we did and have a systematic and evidence-based strategy that we were sure would work.

My research and discussion with leaders in the field led me to the conclusion that lean healthcare was the way forward. This book sets out what is and isn't meant by 'lean'. It aims to dispel some of the myths and show how those approaches that have worked so well in manufacturing industry or in service businesses can also be effective in healthcare. It outlines an approach for getting started on your lean journey, whether this is at the level of the ward, clinic or department, across a patient journey, a whole hospital, or even an entire healthcare system. But first, in case anyone doubts that a radical transformation is needed, let's consider the state of healthcare today.

Just how bad is it?

In 2005, the Department of Health and the National Audit Office in England, together published a document called 'A safer place for patients' (1). This made sobering reading. It showed that one in ten patients admitted to NHS hospitals will be unintentionally harmed. This rate increases if healthcare acquired infections are included. And this is not restricted to the UK. An international review of nine retrospective studies found that this level of patient harm is common across different cultures and different types of healthcare system. Imagine boarding an aeroplane with a 1 in 10 chance of 'harm' being the outcome!

This has been borne out by successive surveys of staff within the NHS. Each year a random sample of all 1.3M NHS staff are surveyed and asked their opinions. Consistently around 40% of staff say that they have seen an error during the month prior to the survey which could have led to harm to patients. **Yes, 40%!**

These issues are increasingly reaching public consciousness. In the UK there have been high levels of anxiety about infection rates, particularly MRSA and Clostridium Difficile. There is a growing awareness that there are unacceptable variations in clinical practice which can lead directly to differences in outcomes for patients.

It's probably not surprising from all of this that despite enormous increases in spending on healthcare in the UK, staff morale does not seem to have improved. 'Doctors and nurses are sick of the NHS' ran a recent national newspaper headline. Professional Associations and trade unions such as the British Medical Association are campaigning vigorously for changes to health policy. Their message is that despite the additional investment staff are working harder than ever before, yet do not see the quality of service or of their own working lives getting any better.

This theme is echoed by political commentators and economists when looking at the value for money provided by health services. They point to the fact that expenditure on healthcare has improved hugely but that productivity, for example as measured by the number of operations carried out compared to staff employed has actually declined.

Of course there are significant difficulties in measuring productivity in a healthcare setting. Hospitals are not factories. Patients are the customers not the raw materials. But there is no doubt that governments and societies around the world are struggling to contain and afford the growing costs of healthcare at the same time as consumers are complaining about its quality.

Productivity is not just about volumes; it is also about outcomes and experiences. Even then adjustments need to be made for the complexity of the cases being dealt with. Ten hip operations on younger, fitter patients are not the same as 10 hip operations carried out on frail, elderly people with a range of complicating co-mobidities.

The productivity question in healthcare also mustn't be confused with that of whether staff are working hard or not. Many staff are working phenomenally hard, but within dysfunctional and chaotic processes. This means that it takes increased amounts of effort just to stand still.

Like many people in my late 40s, I have had elderly parents and parents-in-law who have spent a lot of time in hospital in recent years. As a consequence I have had the opportunity to visit hospitals, not as a healthcare professional but as an actively interested observer. Tahichi Ohno, one of the founding fathers of Toyota, had a somewhat maverick but highly effective way of training young engineers. He used to draw a chalk circle on the factory floor and ask the trainee to stand in it and observe what he saw. Ohno would return, often many hours later, and ask for their observations. His aim was to get them to see the waste, errors and duplication inherent in the processes they were observing.

Anyone who has sat beside a hospital bed for only a small amount of time will have done their own version of the Ohno circle in a healthcare setting. As a relative rather than a healthcare Chief Executive, I was often appalled at what I saw. Staff who spent hours searching for the right equipment, recording information many times over and yet hardly ever having the right pieces of information to hand when they were needed. Teams made up of different professionals with duplicating or even conflicting roles. Patients and relatives who felt ill informed and often helpless in what seemed to them to be a chaotic system.

There is no doubt that many patients and families receive compassionate and effective treatment. There are many of us who have lots of reasons to be grateful to skilled healthcare professionals to whom we owe so much. But there is almost always the sense that those professionals are achieving what they are despite the system rather than with its support.

Attempts at reform

There is a growing movement for improvement in healthcare. Internationally Dr Don Berwick, the President and CEO of the Institute of Healthcare Improvement (IHI) in the USA has led a personal crusade for almost 20 years to encourage those working in healthcare to see the problems and to tackle them head on. The IHI's 100K Lives and 5M Lives Campaigns have led countless healthcare professionals and organisations to adopt more effective clinical practices and to seek out evidence-based approaches to quality improvement. Undoubtedly a great many patients have benefited as a result.

Despite this, however, and even in the face of its 14% GDP spend on healthcare, the USA is ranked as one of the lowest performing healthcare systems in the developed world. 40M US citizens have neither health insurance nor are adequately covered by state backed safety net schemes. The quality of care is highly variable. A recent Commonwealth Fund study noted that the USA ranked last in a six nation comparison of performance on measures of quality, access, efficiency and health outcomes behind Australia, Canada, Germany, New Zealand and the UK (2).

In the UK, the English National Health Service, funded from general taxation and free at the point of delivery, has embodied the principles of equity and social justice in the way that healthcare has been delivered. Historically however the quality and responsiveness of the service has been lacking. Prior to 2001, waits of over a year for operations were not uncommon and each winter saw long queues of patients in emergency departments waiting for admission or treatment.

The NHS plan produced in 2000 set out to tackle this through the twin pronged approach of investment and reform. The investment has certainly been impressive. There was a 56% increase in funding between 2002 and 2007 with spend per head of the population rising from £907 to £1338 (3).

This has been accompanied by an ambitious level of system reform, including the separation of commissioning from providing; the development of a Payment by Results system to reward those hospitals that do more work; the establishment of a regulatory framework that includes the National Institute of Clinical Excellence to set standards and the Healthcare Commission to inspect and regulate. Foundation Status for NHS provider organisations is giving a greater degree of local independence and autonomy. The increased introduction of the independent sector is creating a more truly competitive market. All of this has the potential to force healthcare organisations to confront the fundamental underlying quality and safety issues.

Yet it feels to many observers that the first phase of NHS reform has only tackled the obvious problems. Access times have been greatly improved, staffing levels have been strengthened and outdated buildings and equipment replaced. But the fundamental failings in quality and safety that lie at the heart of healthcare remain almost untouched.

Doctors leaders such as the British Medical Association, Sir Ian Kennedy the Chair of the Healthcare Commission, patient groups and the media have all highlighted failings in reliability, safety and the quality of patients' experience. It is as though the water levels of excess waiting have been lowered and the rocks and boulders of the underlying problems of unsafe practice are now emerging from below the service.

The second phase of NHS reform will need to go much further than the first. It must tackle day-to-day behaviours and deeply embedded clinical practices if it is to achieve transformational improvement.

Why is healthcare like this?

Healthcare is still a craft industry. It is dominated by autonomous professionals or artisans who are self-regulated by professional bodies not unlike the guilds of medieval times. As a consequence there is an almost complete absence of standardised processes. Even when there is agreement between clinicians on best practice, compliance is often poor.

There is a common myth that management is an evil which bedevils healthcare and takes resources away from frontline patient care. In reality the reverse is almost certainly true. There is undoubtedly far too much paperwork, but healthcare is hopelessly under managed in the sense that there is an absence of the active design, delivery and improvement of the processes of care and treatment which patients receive. What is needed is not more administration but better management and leadership which gets to the heart of the way in which care is planned, organised and delivered.

Why might lean help?

Some working in healthcare may well see the assessment in this chapter as too bleak and not accept that a radical transformation is needed. Even those who do accept the analysis might recoil from the phrase 'lean'. It sounds all too much like something dreamt up by management consultants. Many would regard it as something that could be acceptable in manufacturing but will never work in hospitals.

More negatively others see it as 'lean and mean' – paring services back to the bone and making do with less. Overcoming such myths about lean is the first step in assessing whether or not it can really contribute positively in healthcare. What lean is and isn't will be explored in more depth later in this book. For now it is worth noting the successes of the original lean pioneer, Toyota:

- Toyota is the most profitable car manufacturer in the World – in the financial year that ended in March 2007, it made a profit of $13.7 billion, whereas GM and Ford reported losses of $1.97 billion and $12.61 billion respectively in 2006.
- Toyota has been consistently rated by JD Power and other research firms as the top automotive brand in terms of reliability, quality and long-term durability.
- Toyota's market capitalization in May 2007 was $186.71 – more than one-and-a-half times GMs, Fords and Daimler-Chrysler's combined.
- If Toyota meets its forecast sales target of 9.34 million vehicles in 2007, it will officially overtake General Motors to become the world's biggest automobile manufacturer (4).

The premise of this book is that a lean approach can bring about the same levels of transformational improvement in healthcare. Indeed some early healthcare pioneers such as Virginia Mason in Seattle, USA (5), Thedacare in Wisconsin, USA and Flinders in Adelaide, South Australia are showing impressive early results. But as in other sectors this will not be an easy journey nor a quick one and because it is difficult, it is likely that not everyone will achieve the extent of transformation expected.

This book gives some pointers to those who want to make a start. It is not written from the standpoint of a lean expert. I regard myself as having only relatively recently set out on my own lean journey. But as a practising Chief Executive struggling with the pressures and challenges of improving NHS services, I have quickly come to see the immense potential of the lean approach.

We have been testing these ideas and approaches at Bolton Hospital since late 2005. We have had some encouraging early successes. But we now know just how much we don't know. We can see the potential and believe it to be significant but we also believe it will be a long and arduous journey to realise that potential. The aim of this book is to allow others to learn from the first faltering steps that lean healthcare pioneers have been taking, including their mistakes.

The rest of the book is in three sections; section 1 provides a theoretical underpinning and a general discussion of the issues involved in applying lean to healthcare. Section 2 is a 'how to' guide giving pointers for those who want to get started. Section 3 discusses what it takes to embed lean in the healthcare culture and offers some personal reflections on my own lean journey.

References

1. National Audit Office and Department of Health (November 2005) *A Safer Place for Patients: learning to improve patient safety*. London: The Stationery Office.
2. Commonwealth Fund Digest (May/June 2007) *US Health System is no Snow White*.
3. *Hansard* (9 February 2005), Column IS03
4. Steward, T. & Ranon, K. (2007) HBR Interview: Katsuaki Watanbe, *Harvard Business Review*, July–August, pp. 74–83.
5. Bohmer, R. & Ferlins, E. (2006) *Virginia Mason Medical Centre*. Harvard Business School case study number 9-606-044, Revised September 7.

Section One

Can lean work in healthcare?

Most people working in healthcare are resentful of outsiders with little direct experience who think they know how to improve things. Clinical staff rightly regard what they do as special. It takes a great deal of courage and skill to care for people at the most difficult and vulnerable times of their lives. As a result approaches that have worked successfully in motor manufacturing often at first sight appear to be irrelevant to hospitals, clinics and community services.

The first section of this book aims to clear away the mythology that surrounds the lean management approach and to show how it can be creatively adapted into a healthcare setting.

Chapter Two is a basic guide to the ideas behind a lean approach. It shows how lean is focussed on understanding how value is created for the customer by removing wasteful or unnecessary steps. This chapter also describes how Toyota have become the benchmark for any organisation wanting to adopt a lean approach.

Chapter Three points out the marked differences between healthcare organisations and manufacturing businesses. It also shows where there are similarities and how the same tools and techniques can be used to improve processes and outcomes in both settings. The particular cultural challenges of applying lean in healthcare are examined.

Chapter Four is an opening up of possibilities. It paints a picture of what lean healthcare might be like and of the benefits it could bring to staff and to patients. It describes the power of a lean vision event to create this compelling picture of the future which can then be used as a motivating force to secure engagement in your lean transformation.

Chapter Two

What is lean?

SUMMARY

- There are many myths about lean which often create a negative first impression;

- At the heart of lean is an understanding of how value is created for the customer;

- All processes are imperfect and contain steps that do not add value i.e. are waste. Lean is about the continued elimination of waste;

- Toyota is the benchmark for any organisation wanting to adopt a lean approach. Over many decades they have evolved a systematic framework which is as much about culture and beliefs as it is about tools and techniques;

- Successful lean businesses embed this new way of working deep within their organisational DNA.

The myths about lean

Many people have vaguely heard about 'Lean'. When they think about it, their mental image is almost certainly that of an organisation which has been 'slimmed down'. It conjures up the picture of a factory or an office running with almost no people at all. A common anecdote in the post-industrial town in which I live is that the factory of the future is run by a man and a dog. The man's job is to feed the dog and the dog is there to make sure the man doesn't touch the computer.

Given this background, it's hardly surprising that only a passing acquaintance with the term lean tends to have negative connotations. Even those who delve a little deeper usually assume that lean isn't for them unless they are actually working in car manufacturing. The table overleaf sets out some of the most common myths about lean and counter-balances them with the reality.

This chapter describes the main building blocks of a lean approach. It describes how value is created and shows why much of what is done in the work place is actually waste. It explains how over many decades Toyota have gradually evolved a management system which has made them by far the world's most successful lean organisation. Finally, it

Table 1: Myths about lean

Common myths about lean	The reality
• Lean is a recent management fad	• Venetian shipbuilders used a version of lean in the middle ages. Toyota have evolved the Toyota Production System – over a sixty year period
• Lean is about paring back to the bone; 'lean and mean'; less employees are needed	• Successful lean companies adopt a no lay-offs policy; they seek to redeploy staff on to new value adding activity to grow their business
• Lean only works in manufacturing; even then it can only really flourish in Japan where the culture will accept it	• There are many examples of successful lean businesses outside of Japan including service and retail organisations. Tesco – the UK's retailing phenomenon – is a good example of the application of lean principles to both strategy and operations
• Lean is a toolbox of quality improvement techniques	• Such tools are an important part of lean; but the organisational culture and philosophy that surround it are equally vital
• Lean is only for a few technically minded enthusiasts, not for 'ordinary' workers	• In a genuine lean transformation, everyone in the organisation must be fully engaged.

shows how a lean transformation is not complete without the philosophy, mindset and daily behaviours becoming deeply embedded in an organisation's psyche.

How value is created

The starting point for an understanding of lean is the realisation that all work is a process and all processes can be improved. Any work which creates value requires tasks to be conducted in a set sequence.

To give a practical example; I happen to be writing this chapter sat in a hotel bar after dinner (strange what it takes to get the creative juices flowing!). I have just ordered coffee. The process has a number of steps to it which can be broken down in to greater and greater detail. From my stopping at the bar to ask the waitress to bring me a coffee, my finding a table and sitting down, the waitress putting coffee in the espresso machine, operating the machine, finding a cup, putting the coffee in the cup, finding cream, putting both on a tray, bringing them across to me and serving the coffee.

Of course because this is a service transaction, I am interested not just in how long the coffee takes to arrive and whether it is hot when it does, but the intangibles that go with it. Is it served with genuine professionalism and a sincere smile, a half hearted 'have a nice day' or an incoherent grunt?

Lean thinkers call the steps that need to be taken to create a product or service that is valuable to a customer 'a valuestream'. These can be short and simple such as serving my coffee in the hotel bar or longer and more complex depending on the scope that is considered.

The entire value chain for my coffee, for example, may go back all the way to Kenya from the planting and growing of the coffee beans, their harvesting, roasting and grinding, being shipped or flown across the seas, stored in distribution centres, sold by wholesalers and retailers to my hotel chain, all just to be delivered to this hotel bar on this evening, to be placed in my cup of coffee.

Indeed when considered in that way it can be seen that the total valuestream for my after dinner drink may well have taken many months whilst the value added – my drinking of the coffee – will take a few minutes at most. So why might there be so many steps in a value chain and why it might take such a long period of time compared to such a little amount of time value added? The answer is that a great deal of what happens to a product on its valuestream journey (or to the customer in a service business) is not adding value at all. In lean terms it is waste.

The concept of waste

In the real world of work things rarely run smoothly. It is almost always the case that many of the steps taken in a process do not directly add value from the customer's point of view. Sometimes these steps are unavoidable given the current state of our technical capability. They are non-value adding but necessary at the present time. Many other steps, however, will be neither value-adding nor necessary, these are truly waste.

Sadly my hotel bar was busy. After I placed my order the waitress was constantly interrupted and served someone else out of turn. Then she had no clean coffee cups and had to send to the kitchen for more. My request for brown sugar sent her scurrying off to the restaurant as none was stored in the Bar. My coffee eventually arrived late, cold and without the cream I had asked for. As a lean practitioner, I counted the examples of waste and made a mental note to stay somewhere else next time.

The Japanese term for waste is muda. Tahichi Ohno one of the founding fathers of the Toyota production system developed seven different categories for types of waste that are found in the workplace. These are summarised in the table overleaf.

Whatever kind of work you do, whether it is in an office, a shop, a factory or a hospital you can almost certainly see examples of these different types of waste in your day-to-day activity. They are invariably frustrating for staff. Indeed research studies have shown that wasteful activities of this type which staff know are adding little value, are one of the highest causes of work related stress and sickness absence in the workplace.

Table 2: The seven wastes

1. Transport	Unnecessary movement of materials
2. Inventory	Parts or product being stored
3. Motion	Unnecessary movement of workers
4. Waiting	Delays in the process
5. Overproduction	Too much product or service being produced
6. Overprocessing	Unnecessary steps or activities
7. Defects	Errors or deficiencies that require re-work

Once lean practitioners begin to look in detail at the processes of work they often find that an astonishingly large proportion of what is done, actually constitutes waste – sometimes as much as 90 or even 95%! As a result the total time spent looks a little like the diagram below:

Figure 1: Level of waste/value added

Unfortunately most approaches to quality improvement only concentrate on the value adding activities. In my hotel bar example the restaurant might introduce a new state of the art coffee machine that can produce my espresso faster, hotter and more reliably but despite this investment and effort the waste in the system, the delay in finding a cup and, the interruptions which the waitress encounters in bringing me my coffee mean that it is still cold and unpleasant. The effort that the organisation has put in to improving the value-adding parts of the process has not been felt by me as the customer. The waste has got in the way.

Indeed, in the worst cases the investment which has made the value adding activity more efficient can actually leave space for the wasteful activities to increase as shown in the diagram below. e.g. the faster espresso machine just gives my waitress more chatting time with her friend!

Figure 2: Value-adding activity

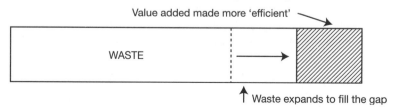

The goal of the lean practitioner is to concentrate on finding and eliminating the waste. This doesn't mean that they aren't interested in improving the value adding activities themselves. In fact because workers are spending less time processing the waste they can turn their ingenuity and creativity to this very task. It also means that they can take on new roles or extra activities which might enhance the quality of the product or service or increase the number of customers served.

Figure 3: Waste reduction

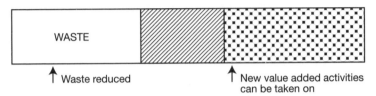

↑ Waste reduced   ↑ New value added activities
                             can be taken on

The origins of waste

So, how does waste come about? Surprisingly one of the main causes of waste in any process is something which intuitively feels more efficient but turns out not to be. This is batching – the placing of tasks, products or even customers in to groups to be processed together all at the same time.

Wherever there is batching there is a queue and wherever there is a queue waste starts to creep in. One of the best family holidays we had was a trip to Walt Disney World in Florida. Although I am not a fan of fun fairs or theme parks, Disney really is something special. The creativity and imagination put in to their rides and other entertainment is awe inspiring. Of course the big thing that everyone complains about even in Disney World is the queues.

At their peak the most popular rides can have queues of one or two hours. Disney World is batching par excellence. Many of the rides have linked carriages that take 20 or 30 people at a time. The queue therefore shuffles forward while batches or 20 or 30 increasingly grumpy parents and over-excited children wait for the next 20 seater capacity car to complete its three minute journey, unload its batch of passengers and take off again.

One of the few rides without a queue is a somewhat old fashioned tour of the park on a slow moving monorail. There isn't the absence of a queue because it is unpopular (indeed it carries a very high volume of passengers many of whom are glad for a place to sit down and rest their feet), but its cars take only 2 passengers at a time. They flow smoothly and continuously around a track without stopping, you simply step in to the next available car as it comes along. The absence of batching speeds up the whole process and avoids the waste of standing in the mid-day Florida sun for 45 minutes with a hyperactive 8 year old.

One of the great challenges in establishing a lean work system is to move from batches and to get a process to flow. This is one of the core revelations that lies at the heart of the move to lean and will be explored in more depth as it applies to healthcare in subsequent chapters.

A second major cause of waste is variability and instability within the process. Sometimes this is a genuine variability in demand, for example the rate at which holiday makers turn up for the different rides at Disney at different points during the day. In some work situations this variability is predictable based on past patterns. In many others the instability is actually a construct of our own processes.

Imagine a small firm producing double-glazing units. Its sales representatives fan out across the region striking deals and securing sales, but these are not transmitted back to the factory immediately so work can start on production. They are grouped together into a weekly and then a monthly order book. This is built into a monthly production schedule which only vaguely resembles the actual pattern of demand from customers wanting double-glazing units. From the point of view of the factory workers this can often feel like rapid swings between feast and famine. The processes are unstable and have huge variation within them, not because customers want their double-glazing units at different times of the month but because the sales processing and production scheduling processes generate an artificial variability.

Understanding the true demand and linking production as closely as possible to it is a core lean concept. The failure to achieve this is a common cause of waste, frustration and resultant poor quality products and services.

So at the heart of a lean approach is the concept of identifying what tasks add value and which are merely waste. Moving from the batching of processes to achieve continuous flow and establishing stability within the work environment are important early steps towards identifying and eliminating waste. But how can an organisation move from these few basic concepts to an over-arching organisational philosophy that builds out from this to create an entirely new way of working. Answering this requires that we study the gold standard for lean organisations – Toyota.

The Toyota Production System

The phrase lean was first coined by two academics James Womack and Daniel Jones in 'The Machine that Changed the World'. (1) They highlighted the growing phenomenon of the Toyota Motor Corporation and gave it the name of 'Lean Production'. Since then Womack and Jones have charted the expansion of lean firstly to other manufacturing companies and then in to other sectors. (2) They have shown how lean can transform service industries and indeed the very way we live our lives (3).

Interestingly Toyota themselves rarely use the phrase 'lean'. On a recent visit to a Toyota factory, our hospital staff were impressed not only by their passion to produce excellent products, but also by their humility. 'We just aim to produce the best cars we can' was the approach of everyone we met. Some lean practitioners would go so far as to say that instead of striving to be lean, organisations should strive to be 'Toyota like'. This is probably something to which Toyota themselves wouldn't subscribe. Above all else they understand that becoming truly lean is about creating a culture: 'first we build people, then we build cars' is the Toyota philosophy.

Understanding the concepts of value and waste is one thing, building a system and a culture which institutionalises the continual elimination of waste and the pursuit of perfect quality is quite another. But this is just what Toyota has achieved. Of course they didn't set out to do this from day one. The Toyota Production System (TPS) evolved over many decades. Gradually over time it has also become the Toyota management system which encompasses everything that they do. Indeed the TPS was only clearly articulated once Toyota began to expand outside of Japan and needed to explain its philosophy and approach to new recruits in foreign lands.

A critical feature of the Toyota approach is that it is a philosophy – a way of seeing the world of work that would be highly unusual in most organisations. It is far from being simply a set of tools and techniques. Jeffrey Liker in his book 'The Toyota Way' explores in depth the different aspects of culture within Toyota that have helped develop and sustain this approach (4).

If Toyota's approach could be reduced to just two principles it would be respect for people and the continued elimination of waste. Genji Gembutsu means 'go to the actual workplace and see for yourself'. In Japanese the gemba is where the work actually happens. All too often in non-lean environments problems are tackled by people who have only a scanty understanding of the actual issues involved (i.e. managers) in offices and meeting rooms, well distant from the actual work place. In a lean organisation, problems are addressed where they arise – in the workplace and by the people who understand the problems best – the workers themselves.

Mr Cho who is now the Chairman of Toyota has said that the Toyota philosophy of management is based on three principles – go see, i.e. actually go and look at the problems for yourself in the actual workplace; ask why – do not give people the solutions but use a questioning and coaching approach to enable them to come up with the answers for themselves; respect people – in Toyota the highest mark of respect is to allow someone to take responsibility for their own actions and not to simply say 'you should, you must or you will'.

The challenge for any organisation wishing to adopt a lean approach is how to emulate the breadth and depth of cultural underpinning put in place by Toyota. To achieve this, the lean leader needs to be a social architect. He or she must be able to envision and design a new kind of organisational entity. One where all the individual elements are effective, but where they also integrate in such a way that their combined effect is much greater than could be expected simply from a sum of their parts. So how can this be done?

Making it part of the DNA

Lots of people know about the Toyota production system. Many have tried to copy it, very few have succeeded. Why is this? Often people assume that adopting the tools and techniques which Toyota use will make them lean. Some go beyond this and see that there is a cultural underpinning to the Toyota approach. So they launch cultural change programmes or issue mission statements to their staff, but very few undertake a detailed, time consuming socialisation of every employee in to a different way of acting and thinking. This is what it takes to embed lean and this is how Toyota do it.

As Toyota themselves say 'it's easier to act yourself in to a new way of thinking than it is to think yourself in to a new way of acting'. At the heart of Toyota's success lies its approach to problem solving. Steven Spears and Kent Bowman have shown how Toyota creates 'a community of scientists' (5). By this they mean that the Toyota way of working is essentially the scientific method applied to problem solving. Perhaps this is why many doctors are becoming increasingly interested in how lean can add value within healthcare.

W. Edward Deeming, the US quality improvement guru who exported many of his ideas to Japan in the 1950s popularised a simple model for problem-solving which embodies the scientific principle of establishing and testing a hypothesis. A variety of acronyms are used to describe it but my own preferred favourite is PDCA – the plan, do, check, adjust cycle.

Figure 4: PDCA cycle

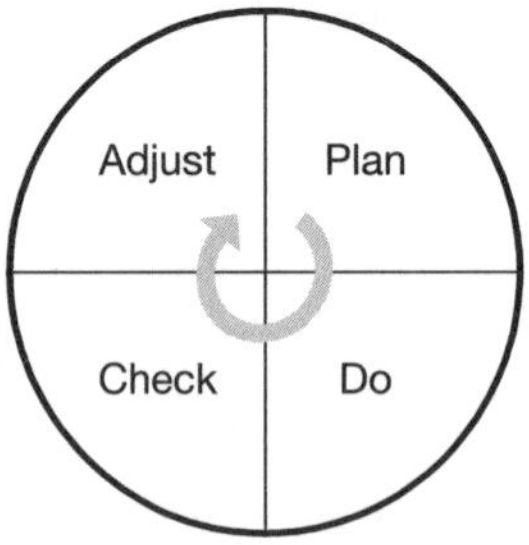

Using the PDCA approach requires discipline and rigor. Firstly it demands that a problem is confronted head on, not worked around, avoided or ignored. The approach begins with the development of a **plan** 'let's try doing X', then testing it out, actually **do** X! Implementing the plan requires change but we don't know whether or not the change is an improvement unless we measure before and afterwards. This is the **check** phase, the use of data to understand the effect of the experiment that has been carried out. The final phase of the cycle is **adjust**. Reflect on what has been done, learn from it and begin a new PDCA cycle all over again.

Toyota use PDCA constantly. Every employee, whether on the shop floor, the design room, or in an office is expected to use PDCA to identify and solve problems in their daily work. The entire Toyota organisation can be thought of as a hierarchy or interlocking PDCA cycles with frontline employees solving problems on a daily basis; supervisors and team leaders grouping these in to bigger cross-departmental or cross-functional problems that require greater effort and reflection to resolve; operational managers tackling more strategic problems that can only be solved on a time horizon of many months; to the highest level executives in Toyota grappling with the long term problems of repositioning a car manufacturing company in an age of concern about fuel emissions and global warming.

This mastering of the PDCA approach is achieved through a massive investment in training and development. This is not simply a few hours in the classroom as is the experience of most employees in most companies. Toyota's approach is one of 'total immersion'. Employees are expected to learn standard work, the routine way of doing things and to stick to it. But they are also expected to identify problems and to seek out and eliminate waste using PDCA and an evidence-based set of problem solving tools and techniques which have been built up over a long period of time.

At the heart of this lies a fascinating paradox, the focus on standard work and high levels of disciplined adherence to this are what actually allows creativity, flexibility and individual responsibility in identifying and eliminating problems. This takes that standard work on to a new level which is more productive, more satisfying and closer to the ultimate goal of a zero defect process.

The aforementioned Mr Cho, now Chairman of Toyota, has said that the TPS should not really stand for the Toyota Production System but for the Thinking Production System. Toyota has built lean in to its cultural DNA by shaping the way all employees think and behave in relation to their work.

So, the challenge for organisations wishing to undergo a lean transformation is an intimidating one:

- First understand what your customers really value and how that value is created

- Secondly learn to see the waste in your processes and find ways to eliminate it

- Thirdly evolve a systematic approach – an organisational architecture that is mutually reinforcing and which will compensate for human frailties

- Fourthly (as if all that wasn't enough!) develop a completely new approach to training and development, problem solving, leadership and management which embeds all this deeply in the DNA of your organisation.

No wonder so few succeed! So how can any of this be at all relevant to healthcare? The next chapter will begin to explore this question.

References

1. Womack, J. Jones, D. & Roos, D. (1990) *The machine that changed the World*. New York: Free Press.
2. Womack, J. & Jones, D. (1996) *Lean thinking: banish waste and create wealth in your corporation*, New York: Free Press.
3. Womack, J. & Jones, D. (2005) *Lean Solutions: how companies and customers can create value and wealth together*, London: Simon and Schuster.
4. Liker, J. (2004) *The Toyota Way: 14 management principles from the world's greatest manufacturer*, New York: McGraw Hill.
5. Spear, S. (2004) Learning to Lead at Toyota, *Harvard Business Review*, May, pp 78–106,

Chapter 3

'We're not Japanese and we don't make cars'

SUMMARY

- Hospitals are not factories and patients are not products. Healthcare has its own unique set of issues that need to be carefully considered;

- At the same time healthcare is a process and all processes can be improved;

- A lean methodology can provide a deeper understanding of how value is created in the healthcare setting and how waste can arise to the detriment of staff and patients;

- Healthcare organisations could emulate Toyota in creating a systematic framework for quality improvement using a lean approach;

- There are particular challenges involved in embedding lean within the culture of a healthcare organisation which need to be tackled.

Why healthcare is different and why it's the same

One morning early in September 2005, I was sitting in a Hospital Seminar Room with a group of Consultant Surgeons. We had just had a lively discussion about the challenges facing the hospital and how we could tackle them. As the hospital was about to explore the use of lean methodology I had been expanding (perhaps on reflection a bit too enthusiastically!) on the successes of Toyota. Fortunately for me the surgeons didn't throw me out of the room. They simply shook their heads and said in a kindly way 'you see we're not Japanese and we don't make cars'.

Of course they were right. A hospital isn't a factory, even though it might be like one in some respects, and patients aren't customers. The giving and receiving of care often isn't a direct financial transaction. In the UK, where healthcare is funded from general taxation and is free at the point of delivery, there is hardly any sense of how the costs of services are being met. Even with insurance-based systems, the money tends to change hands remotely.

What is more, the relationship which a doctor or nurse has with his or her patients is different in many respects from that which a supplier has with a customer. When my own close family have been seriously ill, and thankfully this hasn't been often, I've had no great inclination to demand my consumer rights. What I have wanted is high quality, professional help as quickly as possible.

Patients place a unique level of trust in their care givers, sometimes people they have never met before. They place their hopes, their fears, their wellbeing, sometimes even their lives in someone else's hands. This means that a healthcare experience is highly emotionally charged.

Patients do want a good outcome and whether they achieve this may well affect them for the rest of their lives. But for patients and families the quality of the experience will have an impact on them for the rest of their lives too.

I am lucky that part of my job is that many patients and families write letters of thanks to me for the services that the hospital has provided. Sadly this is often when they have lost a loved one. They are grieving greatly for a much loved mother, father or spouse but they explain how the professionalism of the care and the levels of human compassion showed turned one of the most awful of life's experiences into something which was bearable.

I also receive letters of another kind. Ones where the patient recovered and where the medical cure worked effectively, but where the human experience was traumatic and damaging. The creation of value in a healthcare setting is a complex and difficult issue and I will return to this in detail in Chapter Six, but it is clear that there are many differences between care giving and the manufacture of motor parts.

Why might a lean approach still be applicable?

Perhaps the best way of demonstrating this is to consider the reasons most commonly given as to why lean can't work in healthcare and to see whether or not these hold good (see table opposite).

Healthcare is a process which can be improved by taking a lean approach. But it is different in many ways to an assembly line or a retail outlet. For this reason a lean approach can not be applied dogmatically without any adaptation from a manufacturing setting. It needs to be reinvented for the particular needs of healthcare professionals and the patients and families they serve.

As the table demonstrates, many of the common beliefs about why lean wont work simply don't hold good. The rest of this chapter considers how value is created in healthcare and compares the patient journey to the valuestreams of a lean manufacturing organisation; it shows how waste can arise in a healthcare setting and how this is frustrating and damaging both for staff and for patients; it considers how healthcare organisations can begin to emulate Toyota by creating a systematic framework for lean improvement; finally it begins to consider the particular challenges of embedding a lean approach within a healthcare culture.

How value is created in healthcare

In a previous chapter I showed how value is created through a series of process steps. This is true of all human activity and healthcare is no different. We can see this if we take

Table 3: Summary of differences/similarities

Why healthcare is different	Why it's not
• Caring for patients is not the same as manufacturing products	• This is true…but it is a process and all processes can be improved
• Demand for healthcare is totally unpredictable	• This is not true…patterns of emergency demand are highly predictable by season and by day of the week and the pattern of elective demand is within our control
• The practice of medicine requires great judgement and can't be standardised	• Medicine is a science. Research can determine best practice and has demonstrated that compliance with it improves outcomes
• Every patient is unique	• This is true but many have a great deal in common. Analysis shows that 6% of common conditions account for 60% of the work done in a healthcare setting. Furthermore many patients, even though they have their individual needs, flow through the same processes
• The medical and nursing culture will never accept it	• The early lean healthcare pioneers are demonstrating higher levels of engagement and morale amongst those staff who have been involved in lean activities

one of the commonest aspects of healthcare delivery – a patient presenting at an acute hospital emergency department.

Let us say that I have twisted my knee playing squash (I'm more likely to suffer from a heart attack but let's take the knee for the sake of example). At its simplest the process should be as set out in the diagram below:

Figure 5: A healthcare 'valuestream': how value is added

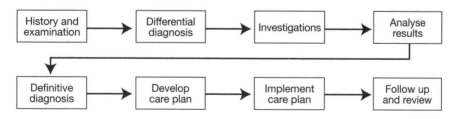

The first thing that would happen would be that a history would be taken and a physical examination conducted. On the basis of this the care giver (it could be a doctor or may be an emergency nurse practitioner) would form a differential diagnosis. This is

23

a hypothesis about what might be wrong with my knee. Then some tests would be requested, this could include xrays or even an MR scan. For other presenting conditions blood tests might have been appropriate and even a range of more invasive procedures such as an endoscopy or exploratory surgery. Once the test results are received, the clinician can proceed to a definitive diagnosis and move to the next step which is the development of a treatment plan. This can be quick and simple i.e. go home, rest and take some paracetamol, or a lengthier process involving, for example, physiotherapy or even corrective surgery. The plan must be implemented effectively and the final step in the process is follow up and review.

The total amount of time involved in this process, which actually adds value to the patient, might be relatively small. Probably a matter of a few minutes for the diagnosis, tests and decision making and perhaps a few hours for the treatment depending on how complicated or serious it was. But the actual time taken for the process can stretch to days, weeks or even months, particularly if corrective surgery is involved, requiring the patient to re-attend the hospital on many separate occasions for outpatient attendances, diagnostic tests and the surgery itself.

Lean practitioners refer to this process as a valuestream i.e. the processes steps that are required to add value from the customers' perspective. To enable this to take place a range of other supporting activities are needed. These do not directly add value from the customers' perspective but are important pre-requisites to support the value-adding process. They are non-value added but essential activity. Examples might include processes for managing the information flow to support the valuestream e.g. the transfer of the patient's previous medical records from a central storage facility to the clinician examining the patient so they are aware of the patient's previous history. Another example might be the process which the organisation has for recruiting, appointing and training staff so that skilled professionals are in place to add the value to the patient as and when they need it.

In effect a hospital is an agglomeration of all of these different types of valuestreams. Whilst some steps and some valuestreams are clearly visible, for example, patients receiving treatment, other steps such as the information flow or the purchasing of goods and services remain largely hidden. An added complication is that the valuestreams flow horizontally through a hospital with patients passing through admissions areas, diagnostic facilities, ward and treatment areas as is appropriate. Hospitals on the other hand are usually organised vertically or functionally into medical specialties and into operational units such as wards, clinics and departments. It is rare indeed for a hospital to have a mechanism for managing the flow of patients through the hospital as a whole and yet it is this that is critical to the quality of the value added.

When considered from the patient's point of view the patient journey or valuestream can begin long before a patient ever arrives at the hospital. It really begins with the patient first realising they have a problem. For example, from the moment I twisted my knee on the squash court. The early part of the journey might have involved visits to my general practitioner, attempts at self-treatment such as painkillers and rest, and it may continue after the hospital episode is finished including, for example, recuperation and convalescence or after hospital care and therapy.

If we are to ensure the greatest possible amount of value is added from the patient's perspective we need to manage the patient journey actively and improve it right from the outset to its completion. This includes the co-ordination, not only of many discreet functions and activities within the hospital setting but of a whole health and social care system involving a wide range of different professional groups, agencies and care providers. The complexity and cultural challenge of this begins to make it clear why there are often errors, problems and waste within the patient journey and why the patient experience is less good than it might be.

Waste in healthcare

The process by which value is added in healthcare is sometimes described as a patient journey, or more often as a clinical pathway. Such clinical pathways are usually described in the abstract. Often they are placed on charts or laminated pieces of card and used to explain the treatment processes which it is intended that patients should receive, as can be seen in the schematic below.

Figure 6: The fantasy patient journey

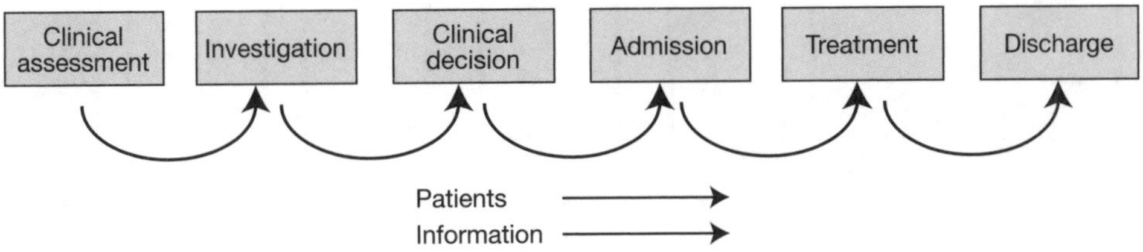

All too often however these are merely fantasy patient journeys. The reality which patients actually experience is far different and looks more like the picture overleaf.

Let's take a case example to examine this is more depth. Imagine a 65-year-old lady called Molly. Molly lives on her own and has been fit and well up until six months ago when she became increasingly breathless. Lately she has had one or two dizzy spells and then a fainting fit. As a consequence her general practitioner has referred her to her local general hospital for an outpatient appointment.

Until she retired two years ago Molly was a senior quality inspector at a local factory that made bread and cakes. She has always had a keen eye for problems and is a bit of an observer of human nature. Following Molly on a journey to her local hospital shows the difference between the fantasy pathway and the real one.

In her old job Molly had been taught about the Seven Wastes and she still looks for them instinctively when she is out and about. It was a long bus ride to her local hospital and Molly did think how much more convenient it would have been if the hospital specialist had been able to come out to the large, well resourced health centre just round the

Figure 7: The patient's journey

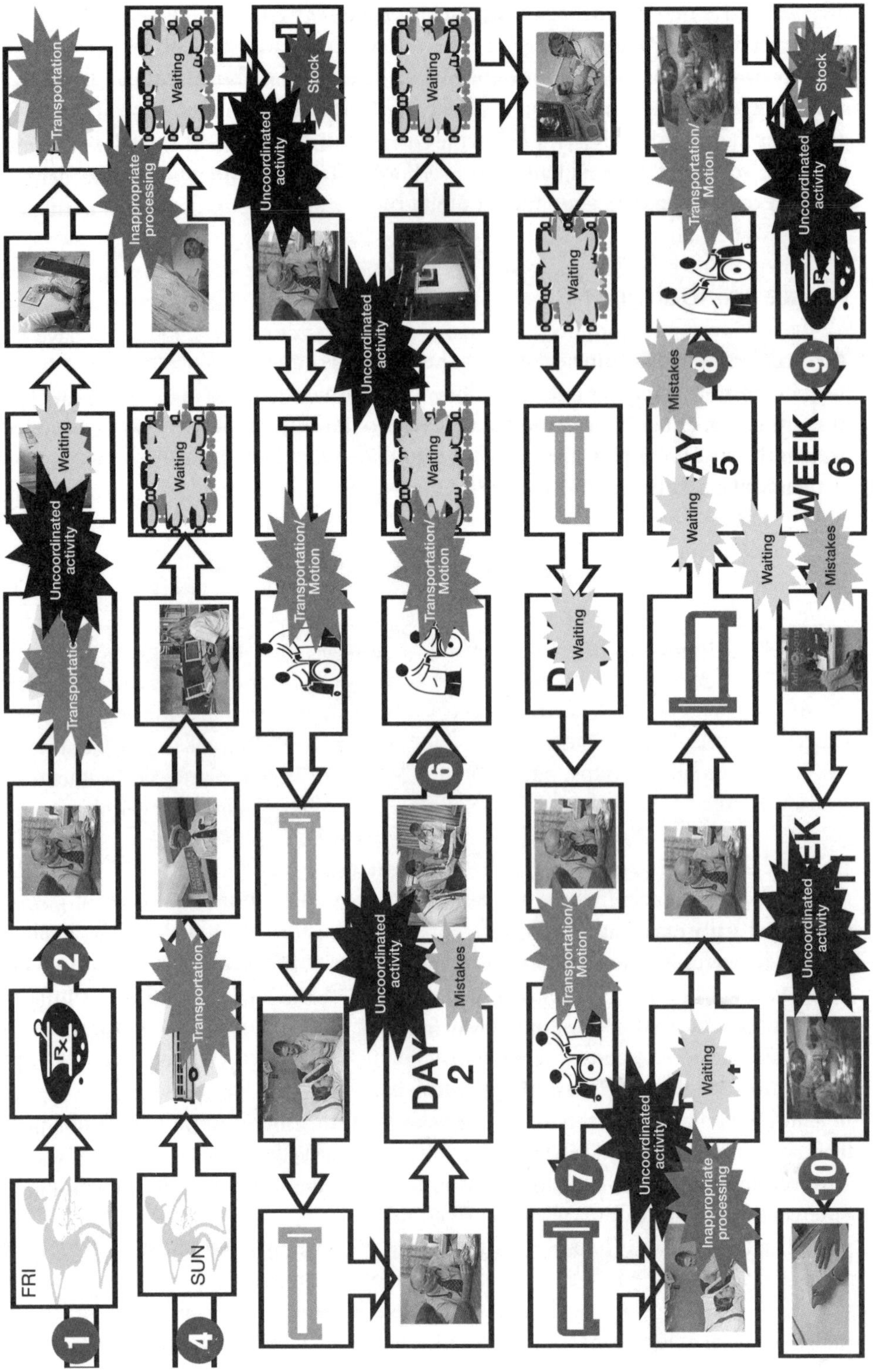

corner from where she lived (Transport). When she got to the hospital, Molly was glad that she had come on the bus, as she saw lots of patients sat in their cars, queuing to find a parking space (Waiting).

The hospital was a large and confusing place and the map which Molly had been sent was out of date (Defect). As a consequence she was a bit breathless when she arrived at the clinic because she'd hurried down the corridor worrying that she was late. She needn't have worried, the clinic had been overbooked (Overproduction, Overburden) and there were lots of patients sat in the waiting room whose appointments were still ahead of Molly's (Waiting).

When Molly booked herself in at the reception desk the receptionist tut tutted and said 'Medical Records haven't sent your paperwork down so I have had to send someone all the way up to the third floor for them. I am afraid your appointment will have to be slid back'. (Defects, Waiting, Motion).

Molly had a long wait but it did allow her to catch up on reading the library book that she'd brought with her. She also noticed how busy and harassed the Reception staff seemed to be. Her friend who worked in a clinic had told her they had to note down patients details three times – once on paper and on two different computer systems. No wonder they were grumpy! (Over-processing).

When she was finally shown in to the consulting room it was small and cramped, mainly because there were a large number of cardboard boxes stacked at one end. The nurse apologised for this but explained that the supplies department only delivered to the department once a week and they had no storage space (Inventory).

Molly was eventually seen by a somewhat harassed junior doctor who was muttering under her breath about having to see ten more patients that morning than she'd expected (Overburden). The doctor decided that she needed to take some blood tests.

The clinic's phlebotomist had rung in sick and not been replaced so the doctor had to do it herself (Defect). Unfortunately it took her three attempts to get blood out of Molly's vein which made her arm really sore (Defect). Eventually the nurse took over from the doctor and got a blood sample straight away.

The doctor scribbled something on Molly's notes and left the room. The nurse said to Molly 'I am afraid that this doctor is still in training. She seems to have asked for you to have an awful lot of tests done but I suppose she is just being cautious' (Over-production) 'You'll need to come back to the hospital quite a few times for this little lot, you'd better talk to reception on the way out'. (All 7 Wastes to be repeated again on the next visit!).

Molly's story would probably be familiar to anyone who has been a patient recently in a hospital anywhere in the world. Far from the lean concept of waste not applying in healthcare it's endemic! The observant reader will also have noticed an extra waste – 'Overburden'. This is the stress that is placed on staff in a non-lean system and is known in Japanese as 'Muri'.

In healthcare terms the seven wastes can be described like this:

Table 4: Examples of waste

Waste	Healthcare examples
Transport	Excessive movement of patients and equipment
Inventory	Unnecessary high levels of ward stocks
Motion	Staffing walking miles to carry out tasks
Waiting	Patients on waiting lists and in waiting rooms
Overproduction	Unnecessary tests and xrays
Over-processing	Multiple history taking
Defects	Medication errors; wrong site surgery
And the 8th waste – overburden	The stress and frustration caused for overworked staff

The causes of waste in healthcare have many similarities to those in other kinds of organisations. The batching of activities in groups, instability and variability within the processes, the existence of process bottlenecks and lack of co-ordination in supporting processes all create waste and make for a stark difference between the fantasy journey and the real journey.

Batching

As was described in the previous chapter, grouping activities, products or even patients into batches is a natural human inclination. It feels more efficient but in reality it isn't. In healthcare batches can be seen everywhere: patients sat in waiting rooms, xray films waiting to be reported, tests in the laboratory waiting to be processed, appointment letters waiting to be issued. Just as in manufacturing, putting processes in to flow is a big leap forward in identifying and eliminating waste. Unfortunately this isn't as easy as it sounds!

One of the earliest lean experiments which we tried in our own hospital was on the day surgery ward. This is for patients who need only relatively minor operations often under local anaesthetic and without an overnight stay. Traditionally these patients have been organised in to a morning and afternoon 'batch'.

The morning batch have all been asked to turn up at the hospital at 7.30am. The surgeon and anaesthetist need to see the patients before they operate on them. The patients are asked to get undressed and lie on a bed on the ward. The surgeon and anaesthetist then do a quick round spending two or three minutes with each patient so that the first operations can start at 9am.

The operations are usually relatively quick and simple and in total nine patients may be treated in a single morning. Of course the last patient in the queue will be lying on a bed for almost four hours waiting for their operation.

As an experiment we tried to put these patients into flow. Instead of being asked to arrive as a batch at 7.30am, they were given timed appointments staggered throughout the morning. The anaesthetist and the surgeon (who had been involved in the planning of this) came out of theatre in between cases to see the next patient immediately before the operation began.

The effect on the day surgery ward was almost magical. Patients no longer needed to lie on beds before their operation and so didn't need nurses to look after them. They could come in, sit in a comfortable chair, get undressed just before their operation began and have less time being either bored, or more likely, worried about what was going to happen to them.

The result was that the Day Surgery ward could save 50% of its floor space because it now needed beds only for those patients who had already had their operations. It also saved 40% of the nursing time as it only required a nurse to receive the patient and take their details, not keep an eye on them whilst they were waiting for their operation. The feedback from the patients was certainly positive.

Putting the patients in to flow had had an immediate and dramatic effect on the level of resources and on the patient experience. The difficulty in sustaining this however was that not all operations were as simple and straight-forward as the ones on the morning in question. This made it difficult for the surgeon and the anaesthetist to create the time to come out of theatre to assess the patient immediately before the operation began.

A valuable lean lesson had been learned. Each step in the process links to the next. Whilst we had greatly improved the process on the day surgery ward we ran the risk of making the day surgery theatres less effective and efficient and it may be that the over-all patient journey would suffer as a result.

We went back to the drawing board to improve the whole of the process rather than just the ward itself. The lesson was clear, putting patients in to flow rather than batching them was better for the patient, and technically far more efficient. But it needed careful planning and moving directly to one patient flow might not be feasible.

A good start is to reduce batch sizes, perhaps by halving them initially and dealing with the problems that this identifies and then continuing to do this through a number of cycles of improvement, moving ever closer towards the goal of one piece or one patient flow.

Instability

It is certainly true that there is variability in the demands placed on a hospital's services. Some of this relates to genuine fluctuations in patients' needs. Hospital emergency departments are at their busiest in the evenings and Fridays and Saturdays are periods of peak activity (particularly if the local football team has been playing at home!).

This variability undoubtedly leads to waste. Patients are more likely to be kept waiting and errors are more likely to occur at times when the emergency department is at its busiest. However although the demand for healthcare fluctuates, it does so to a remarkably consistent pattern. Historical analysis shows that the patterns of ambulance arrivals and of walk in patients at the A&E Department are predictable by time of day, day of week and the month of the year.

Even more sophisticated predictive models can be applied. There is strong evidence demonstrating that the number of hospital admissions changes in direct correlation to the ambient temperature as this can affect both respiratory and circulatory conditions. Hospitals are therefore able to use Meteorological Office forecasts to estimate with some accuracy changes in demand for their emergency services. So, although there is variability in emergency demand it can be predicted and planned for.

Perhaps surprisingly a great deal of the variability of the demand within healthcare is self-induced rather than relating to fluctuations in demands from patients. The NHS Modernisation Agency in the UK examined the variation in emergency and elective admissions (1). Elective admissions are planned ones which are ostensibly under the control of the hospital.

The Modernisation Agency concluded that there is a great deal more variation in elective admissions than in emergency ones. This is because this process is not effectively scheduled and managed. It has grown up over time and is based on the aggregate impact of the operating schedules of each individual surgeon.

Most hospitals do not have systems which effectively link patterns of emergency and elective demand and schedule appropriate theatre space, beds, critical care and staffing at the appropriate times. Furthermore because most hospitals do most of their planned work on a Monday to Friday basis, this gives a huge variability by day of the week.

Another example of hospital induced variability is the variability in discharge processes. Again you would imagine that these were more under the control of the hospital and so less variable than admissions, but in reality this doesn't appear to be the case. Analysis by the NHS Modernisation Agency of the variability between discharges and admissions in a typical hospital showed that discharges varied much more widely.

This is because they are a product of the internal processes of the hospital and of its partners, including the way medical staff conduct ward rounds, the availability of equipment and staff to produce and analyse test results and the fact that most hospitals are not geared up to discharge patients at the weekends when there is also a lack of primary care and social care support in the community.

This instability within healthcare's processes, both natural and induced by the way the systems are organised generates enormous amounts of waste and creates significant potential for error and harm.

Process bottlenecks

If you take a walk around a manufacturing plant you can often see a bottleneck through which lots of parts need to be processed. These are usually large and expensive pieces of equipment. It is common to see long queues of parts coming from different parts of the factory and waiting as inventory before this piece of equipment for processing.

Such items are known to lean practitioners as 'monuments' and they can be causes of significant delays and of waste. Healthcare has lots of monuments! Perhaps the most visible example are radiology departments. These contain expensive high tech equipment such as MR and CT scanners. Many different types of patients require access to these facilities whether they are outpatients or inpatients, planned treatments or emergencies.

As a consequence there are often queues of patients waiting to be processed through the radiology facilities. This can lead to long delays in appointments for planned treatments. It can also add many days to a patient's length of stay in hospital. This then creates a further cycle of error and waste as those patients who are in hospital longer than they need be may pick up an infection or become less mobile and more dependent, thereby entering a cycle of decline.

Of course monuments aren't necessarily capital equipment. Sometimes consultant medical staff themselves can become monuments. If patients are lying in a bed waiting for a twice weekly ward round from a consultant physician before they can be discharged, the physician is acting as a monument or process bottleneck and queues of patients inevitably form around him or her.

Uncoordinated support processes

Most newspapers when they talk about healthcare refer to doctors and nurses. Some occasionally get as far as therapists, very few seem to understand the complexity of healthcare and the vast range of professions and disciplines that are needed to make a hospital run smoothly. This includes everyone from health records clerks, porters and cleaners to supplies staff, computer operators and chaplains.

Many of these support functions have often been given a low priority within the hospital hierarchy. They receive relatively little management attention, yet waste and delays in these support processes can frustrate the best designed clinical system and mean that the patient receives poor care despite the best efforts of skilled professionals. It doesn't matter how good the surgeon is if there are not enough porters to get the patients to theatre on time.

Quality improvement in healthcare

Those interested in quality improvement in healthcare have been striving to address these challenges for well over a decade. The Institute of Healthcare Improvement based in Boston USA have pioneered the application of quality improvement tools in a healthcare setting. They have encouraged hospital managers and clinicians to borrow from disciplines such as operational research, to understand and redesign their processes. They have also lately begun to promote the potential value of adopting an overall lean philosophy (2).

Between 2001 and 2004 the NHS Modernisation Agency in the UK also promoted these approaches. The significant improvement in the timeliness of the admission of emergency patients in England was supported by the adoption of the lean principles of flow and streaming as encouraged by the emergency services collaborative.

Subsequently the Modernisation Agency's successor, the National Institute for Innovation and Improvement has continued to promote these types of approaches. Similar initiatives have been pioneered with good results in the Netherlands, Scandinavia, Australia and other parts of the world. As a consequence there is a growing movement of clinicians and managers who are interested in quality improvement in healthcare.

Sadly they still represent a minority of their profession, albeit an energetic and enthusiastic one. As a consequence most of the successes which have been achieved have been in relation to particular services or conditions. There are few examples of whole organisational transformation in healthcare.

Where this has occurred those organisations have had a coherent philosophy of quality improvement that has been sustained consistently over a long period of time. In effect they have succeeded in developing the equivalent of 'the Toyota Production System' for healthcare … a Toyota-style hospital. If lean is to succeed in healthcare and to support genuine transformation, then it must be as part of a coherent philosophy and a systematic approach.

Embedding lean in the healthcare DNA

To talk of a healthcare culture is perhaps a misnomer. It is more properly described as a collection of sub-cultures. Hospitals are made up of differing professional tribes. Each has their own history, training, hierarchy and rituals. This of course includes medics, nurses, therapists, scientists, managers, support workers and others, but even within the professions there are important nuances and distinctions. Behaviours and attitudes differ within medicine, for example, between physicians, surgeons, anaesthetists and radiologists, not to mention the cultural and philosophical divide between community based primary care physicians and hospital doctors.

What is needed is a common language and philosophy which can unite the different groups and align them behind a common purpose. This is critical to achieving the multi-professional and multi-disciplinary teamwork which is so essential to success in a hospital setting. The early experience of lean healthcare pioneers is that lean can provide this unifying force. There are a number of reasons for this:

- Lean is based on the scientific method
- It involves the collection of data and the testing of hypotheses
- It is focused on the patient, i.e. improving value for the customer
- It aims to make professional working lives easier as well as meeting the organisations goals
- It makes visible to senior management problems which are often experienced on a day-to-day basis by frontline clinicians

For a lean methodology to become the shared language and mindset of a healthcare organisation requires extensive exposure and training of staff in the tools, techniques and behaviours. Week long rapid improvement events are a powerful intervention for achieving this as will be discussed later in Section Two. It also demands a fundamental rethink on the behalf of senior management about what management and leadership is for in the organisation and what those leaders and managers will actually do. This is explored in greater detail in Chapter 10.

So, can lean work in healthcare? The early evidence from healthcare pioneers is that it can. Steven Spears, a Harvard Academic who has studied Toyota in depth most certainly believes that the principles are transferable to a healthcare setting (3) He cites examples from a number of US based hospitals including the University of Pittsburgh Medical Centre (Shadyside) and the Virginia Mason Medical Centre in Seattle.

Virginia Mason have been on their lean journey since 2001 and large numbers of senior managers and clinical staff have visited Japan to see the benefits of lean for themselves at first hand. Virginia Mason report extensive benefits as a result, including reductions in inventory costs, improvements in productivity, significant reductions in defects in the patient care process and cumulative savings of at least $12 million (4).

The Institute for the Healthcare Improvement themselves, the leading exponents of quality improvement in healthcare worldwide have also promoted the positive benefits of a lean approach (5). They quote the example of Thedacare based in Appleton Wisconsin in the USA where again the early results have been impressive. $3.3 million of savings in 2004, accounts receivable reduced from 56 to 44 days equating to about $12 million in cash flow, the redeployment of staff from non value-adding work to work of higher value.

Recently Thedacare have developed a 'model line', their collaborative care ward, which they are using to demonstrate the power of lean (6). The results in this area have been particularly impressive:

Table 5: Thedacare collaborative care ward

	Percentage improvement
Medication reconciliation errors	99%
Patient satisfaction	21%
Length of stay	34%
Cost per case	37%

Lean Healthcare Pioneers are not restricted to the USA. Flinders Hospital based at Adelaide in South Australia has also been using a lean approach to improve the hospital's performance and the quality of care delivered to patients. Their 'Redesigning Care Programme' is founded on lean thinking. It has dramatically improved the process of emergency admissions to the hospital, allowing them to keep pace with significant increases in demand. What's more it has improved the quality of the care that is delivered, reducing the number of adverse incidents and of litigation claims arising from errors (7).

In the UK, the NHS Confederation (a membership association for UK Hospitals and Primary Care Trusts) has been encouraging the adoption of a lean approach. Whilst UK hospitals are not as far advanced on their journey as others elsewhere in the world, the early results from places like Bolton, the Wirral and Hereford indicate that any cultural problems that might exist in transplanting the methodology into a UK context can be overcome (8, 9).

This chapter has demonstrated how a lean approach can be applied in a healthcare setting. So what could be the end product if we were to take lean logic to its ultimate conclusion for a whole hospital or an entire healthcare system? This question will be explored in the next chapter.

References

1. NHS Modernisation Agency (2004) *Ten High Impact Changes for Service Improvement and Delivery*, London: Department of Health.
2. Institute of Healthcare Improvement (IHI) (2005) *Going Lean in Healthcare*, Cambridge, MA: IHI.
3. Spears, S. (2005) Fixing healthcare from the inside today, *Harvard Business Review*, September.
4. Ollier Weber, D. (2006) Toyota Style Management drives Virginia Mason, *The Physician Executive*, January/February.
5. IHI, ibid.
6. Touissaint, J. (July 2007) Presentation to Global Lean Healthcare Summit, Warwick UK.
7. Ben-Tovim, D. (2007) Lean thinking across a hospital: redesigning care at the Flinders Medical Centre, *Australian Health Review*, 31(1), pp 10–15.
8. Jones, D. & Mitchell, A. (2006) *Lean Thinking for the NHS*, London: NHS Confederation.
9. Fillingham, D. (2007) Can lean save lives? *Leadership in Health Services*, Vol 20, No 4, pp 231–241.

Chapter 4

What would lean healthcare look like?

SUMMARY

- In lean healthcare there would be no needless deaths or harm, no needless suffering, no delays, no waste, no inequalities and no feelings of helplessness;

- Each step in the lean healthcare journey would be perfectly designed and executed according to lean principles;

- These steps would be actively managed to create a smoothly flowing patient journey; the job of healthcare institutions would be to orchestrate those journeys and the infrastructure needed to support them;

- A 'Lean Vision Event' is a way of engaging all stakeholders in building a picture of lean healthcare and developing a plan to deliver it.

It's not too difficult to see how the success of a lean manufacturer, such as an automobile maker, can be measured. Reductions in scrap, rework and inventory, improvements in the quality and reliability of vehicles and shorter lead times all lead to higher customer satisfaction, sales and profitability. It isn't quite so easy to define what a lean hospital or a healthcare system would be like.

The Institute of Medicine in the USA has produced an ambitious blueprint for healthcare in the 21st century (1). Their guiding principles are that perfect healthcare should be:

- Safe
- Effective
- Timely
- Efficient
- Equitable
- Patient-centred

Don Berwick, the Founder and President of the Institute of Healthcare Improvement has expressed these in more memorable terms. He has stated that the perfect healthcare system would be one where there are:

- No needless deaths or harm
- No needless suffering
- No delays
- No waste
- No inequalities
- No feelings of helplessness

I am sure that is a system in which we would all like to be a patient or to work as a member of staff. As we have already seen in Molly's example in chapter 3, the reality today is often far from that.

Taking just one dimension, that of timeliness, we can see how far we currently are from the ideal. The National Health Service in the UK has a goal of delivering planned treatment for all patients within an 18-week period by the end of 2008. This is counted as starting from the patient attending their primary care practitioner knowing that they have a problem, knee pain for example, through the variety of specialist assessments and diagnostic tests, through to the onset of definitive treatment.

Even as recently as 2006 that whole process could have taken almost twelve months, including a three month wait for an outpatient assessment, a similar or longer wait for diagnostic tests such as x-rays or CT scans and up to a six month wait for an operation should one be needed.

Even for hospitals that succeed in delivering the 18-week maximum journey time the process might still look something like this:

Figure 8: Patient journey for day case knee surgery: NHS 2008

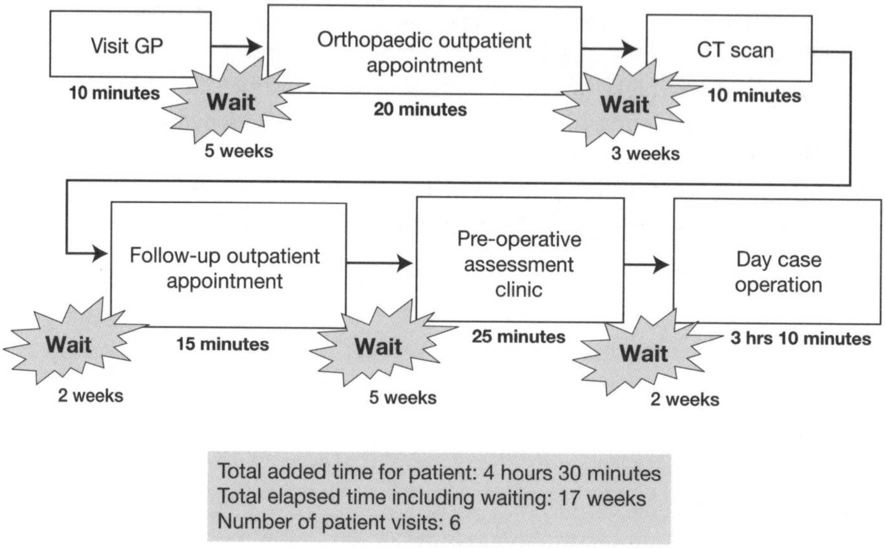

Total added time for patient: 4 hours 30 minutes
Total elapsed time including waiting: 17 weeks
Number of patient visits: 6

Total elapsed time for the patient would be 17 weeks, whilst the value added time to correct the knee problem is only 4 hours 30 minutes. This has also involved six separate visits for the patient with all the attached inconvenience, time needed off work, and so on.

What's more as we saw in Molly's story in the previous chapter the chances of that patient journey being error free are slim indeed! Lost records, cancelled appointments, delays in theatre and even medication errors or infections can all impact adversely on the quality of the patient's experience. The fact that staff are working in a stressed and busy environment may also mean that the human dimensions of the care received are less ideal than would be wished.

One hospital, Thedacare in Wisconsin in the USA, has demonstrated what a similar experience might be like in a lean healthcare system. Thedacare have fundamentally redesigned their orthopaedics service along lean principles, creating what they refer to as 'orthopaedics plus'. The service has been designed to flow smoothly with unnecessary steps and waste being eliminated. A careful calculation of demand has been made and steps have been taken to match the capacity closely to it so that waits and delays do not build up. The process in Thedacare for a similar condition is as follows:

Figure 9: Patient journey for day case knee surgery: Thedacare 2008

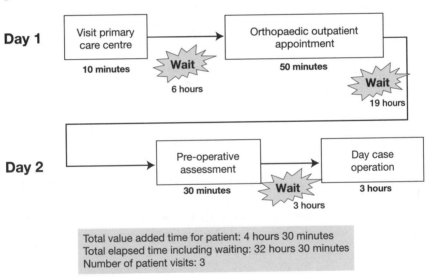

This equates to just 32½ hours of elapsed patient time for the same value added time of 4 hours 30 minutes. A significant improvement over the NHS equivalent!

Thedacare have also set themselves an ambitious goal of a 50% reduction in identified defects year on year. This means an ever-decreasing likelihood that the patient experience will be marred by the errors or waste that are currently found in existing healthcare systems.

So how can such a lean future become a reality in our clinics, surgeries and hospitals? The steps that need to be taken are as follows:

Figure 10: Necessary steps

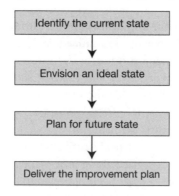

Firstly it is necessary to understand the present patient journey with all its inherent waste, errors, delays and duplication. The second step is the opportunity to let creativity run riot! The visioning of an ideal state is intended to free up thinking and create a picture of just how perfect healthcare could be if there were no constraints on technology, staffing or resources. The future state brings us back to the real world. It should be set some one to two years in the future to make it challenging but achievable to realise. It should be defined in much more concrete terms. The improvement plan is then the process of getting there.

The way in which this journey of lean redesign can best be undertaken and some of the tools and techniques that will help are set out in more detail in Section Two of this book. The rest of this chapter will explore what the elements of a lean future state might be at the level of a ward, clinic or department, a hospital or a whole healthcare system.

The building blocks of lean healthcare

The patient journey within lean healthcare will be one where all the steps are necessary and add value and where they are linked together in such a way that the patient flows smoothly without delay or interruption. What's more the information, staff and resources that are needed for their successful care and treatment will all be present at just the right time.

The patient journey can be thought of as a series of lean healthcare 'cells' i.e. discrete activities and functions through which the patient passes. These need to be co-ordinated carefully to ensure that the patient can flow smoothly between them with the minimum of hassle and delay.

Supporting this patient journey are a number of other processes or valuestreams which are often hidden to the patient. These include the provision of information and of goods and supplies, the recruitment and training of staff and the financing of the whole enterprise. It is the job of healthcare institutions in a lean environment to ensure that those lean healthcare cells are effectively designed and linked together and that the supporting processes are also grounded in lean principles.

Healthcare institutions such as hospitals sit within wider healthcare systems that include primary care practitioners, community services, and social care support as well as patients themselves and their families and other resources. In a lean world these too would be synchronised and be designed according to lean principles. Let us take each of these elements in turn.

The lean healthcare 'cell': lean wards, clinics and departments

In a manufacturing environment the first step on the road towards a lean transformation is to create work cells that are based on lean principles. This often means altering the physical layout of machinery to reduce batch sizes and to create flow. Some Japanese sensei when advising western firms have made dramatic gestures such as moving all the equipment in a machine shop overnight on to a lean layout! This might not be possible within a hospital setting but the aim must be to design the building blocks of the clinical process – the work of clinical teams in wards and departments – along lean lines.

Simpler Consulting work in partnership with businesses to support lean transformations. They have been helping Bolton Hospital with the application of lean principles to healthcare since 2005. The key elements which Simpler suggest should be built in to any lean design are captured in the diagram below:

Figure 11: Lean tools/principles

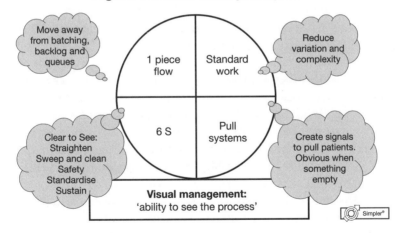

What would these elements mean in a healthcare context?

• Firstly the establishment of one piece or one patient flow – This is a radical departure for most healthcare processes which depend upon batching backlogs and queues in order to control demand.

- Standard work – This is about the reduction in variation and complexity with the same processes being done consistently in the same way every time. This is unusual to say the least in a healthcare setting. It is not uncommon for every consultant to have their own method of doing ward rounds and every nursing team to adopt a different approach to handovers at the end of a shift.

- 6S – This is a technique for ensuring that the workplace is calm, orderly, tidy and set up for flow at all times. Not many hospital wards are like this! The first impression when walking on most of them is of clutter and untidiness and in the worst cases, almost a sense of chaos.

- Pull Systems – Again it is rare for wards to ring the admissions office or Accident and Emergency Department asking for patients because they have empty beds. In most hospitals patients are pushed on to wards by 'bed management' teams under pressure from over-crowding in the emergency department.

- The final lean principle is that of Visual Management – this refers not just to charts and control boards displaying information about performance (although these are necessary and often lacking). It also relates to other visual cues. A flashing light above a patient's bed when they have pressed the call bell is a good example.

In the UK, the National Institute of Innovation and Improvement has been working with four hospitals; Luton and Dunstable, Barnsley, Royal Liverpool and Broadgreen and Basingstoke and North Hampshire to redesign ward environments along lean principles. The programme is known as 'The Productive Ward'.

Research conducted at the outset made for depressing reading. Only 27% of the ward staff believed that their ward was well or very well organised. The main problems were cited as being staffing levels, too much paperwork and poor morale. 73% of the nurses questioned believed that they were not able to spend as much time as needed on direct patient care and that this had an adverse impact both on quality and on job satisfaction.

Over a period of months Lean Consultants worked with the four sites to improve flow, use 6S to reorganise the ward environment and to reduce wasteful activity. Achievements included improvements in meal times, in drug rounds and in shift handovers. The result was more time available for nurses to spend with patients and a more involved and motivated workforce (2).

At Bolton Hospital we have also seen benefits from applying lean principles at the level of the clinical team within a ward environment. One of our earliest developments was that of a trauma stabilisation unit, an eight-bedded bay within one of our orthopaedic wards.

- Patients were streamed upon admission into simple and complex and the most complex patients with co-morbidities and medical as well as orthopaedic problems were placed on the Trauma Stabilisation Unit (TSU).

- A multi-disciplinary team of staff including doctors, nurses, therapists and social workers worked together to standardise processes and streamline paperwork (Standard Work).

- Batch sizes were reduced for example the ortho-geriatrician moved from weekly rounds on the ward to shorter, daily ward rounds (Flow).

- Trauma co-ordinators were empowered to seek out poorly patients entering via A&E or languishing elsewhere on orthopaedic wards who needed the care of the TSU (Pull).

- The physical layout of the TSU was re-organised. It included, for example, colour coded boxes at each bedside in which the main items needed for that patient could be stored. This saved on nursing time walking backwards and forwards to the main store area. The colours on the bedside store boxes matched colour codes in the main storeroom too which speeded up replenishment when that needed to take place (6S).

- A visual management display was developed to give the ward team greater control of patient care interventions and to keep track of the co-ordination needed between the different specialties and disciplines (Visual Management). I will review this case example in Lean Section 2 in more depth as the TSU was only one element of a much wider redesign of the trauma patient pathway in Bolton. For now it is worth noting that the results over a nine month period were spectacular. They included a 33% reduction in length of stay for this group of patients, a 42% reduction in paperwork and most importantly of all a 38% reduction in mortality. Over 60 lives have been saved in under two years as a result of the application of lean principles to this group of patients.

The creation of lean work cells isn't just an issue for wards. The building blocks of the patient journey need to be constructed along lean lines, whether this be in clinics, theatres, emergency rooms or other areas where staff are in direct patient care contact. Lean principles also need to be applied in departments that provide clinical support processes such as pathology and pharmacy, or non clinical support areas such as laundry, catering, finance or human resources.

Examples of lean cells within Bolton Hospital:
- Pathology: a lean blood sciences laboratory has been created which has dramatically reduced the turnaround times of tests and improved efficiency
- Radiology: a plain film reporting cell has been developed which is preventing the build up of films waiting to be reported or reports on tape waiting to be typed
- Laundry: process redesign has decreased waste and costs, increased income and greatly improved working conditions in what was previously an unpleasant environment
- Finance: the creditors section have used lean to support a move towards a paperless process.

Lean specialists refer to these types of improvements as 'Point Kaizen'. Kaizen being the Japanese phrase for continuous improvement. Such activities are well worth doing. They bring benefits in decreased costs, improved quality and better staff morale. But the overall benefit to patients from Point Kaizen is at the end of the day limited, because the whole process may still be suboptimal.

There is no point getting the x-rays reported in six hours as opposed to two days if consultant ward rounds are still weekly, so no decision is made on the more rapidly produced xray result. Similarly if problems with transport, pharmacy, health records or other support functions still create waste, errors and delays, this might mean that the patient does not feel the benefit from the improvements which have been delivered. Consequently Point Kaizen activities are much more powerful when joined together in the redesign of an overall patient journey known in lean terms as a valuestream.

The lean patient journey or valuestream

If we return to our earlier example of trauma, the Trauma Stabilisation Unit is only one part of the patient's journey. Patients typically spend only a few hours there being medically stabilised prior to their operation. During their passage through the hospital they are also likely to directly experience, the A&E department, x-ray, a general orthopaedic ward, theatres, a postoperative ward and the discharge lounge.

The challenge in turning this patient journey in to a lean one is to understand each of these steps and to ensure they are designed on lean principles. The information that supports them and the steps themselves need to be co-ordinated to support a smooth continuous flow. This is what Bolton set out to do in order to improve the trauma journey.

Mortality rates for trauma in Bolton had historically run at a level higher than the national average. In 2005, the relative adjusted of risk of death from a fractured hip in Bolton was 174 (compared to a national average of 100). To deliver the necessary improvements a future state plan was developed for the whole of the trauma patient's journey.

Improvement events were run in all of the areas described above. It became clear that there were a large number of staff involved in the patient journey. Historically however these staff had not been conscious of themselves as part of a single system or seen themselves as a team pulling in the same direction. The lean redesign of the trauma journey was important not only in ensuring the new service reflected lean principles but in engaging and involving the different groups of staff who were necessary to the effective care of the patient.

Six-week long rapid improvement events were run involving over ninety staff including doctors, nurses, therapists, social workers, radiographers, managers and clerical support staff. Latterly a mission control centre has been established to track how effectively the whole valuestream is performing.

Significant gains can be made by moving from Point Kaizen to Flow Kaizen – that is from just establishing lean cells to linking them together in to a lean patient journey.

But patient journeys don't exist in isolation. Patients with different conditions pass through the same facilities. Many staff deal with different kinds of patients on a continuing basis. The interaction between these different patient journeys therefore needs to be co-ordinated. The shared facilities through which they pass need to be managed effectively. There needs to be a momentum and support for continuous quality improvement to enable the patient journey to flow smoothly. These functions are the task of the leadership in a lean hospital.

The lean hospital

Hospitals are curious institutions. I was once told by an experienced senior NHS manager that it was best to think of them as being made up of feudal baronies. These were the various medical specialties each headed by a powerful group of senior (often older!) clinicians.

These baronies are organised vertically and hierarchically, but patient journeys flow laterally across the hospital. There is therefore a need for these baronial fiefdoms to collaborate and synchronise their activities. A single patient may experience a whole variety of specialties including emergency medicine, anaesthesia, orthopaedic surgery, radiology, pathology, geriatric medicine, as well as a range of non-medical specialties such as nursing, occupational therapy, physiotherapy, pharmacy and many others.

A lean hospital needs to build a consensus vision which these professional groups can share about its underlying aims, values and the principles on which it will be organised. It needs to identify its high volume patient flows and decide how these will be managed. It also needs to consider its supporting processes whether these be human resources, financial, information or the supply of goods and services and ensure that these support a lean approach to healthcare.

A powerful way of building a lean vision and plan is through an enterprise-wide valuestream analysis event. This is undoubtedly a bit of a mouthful! In Bolton we renamed it our Lean Vision Event. The Lean Vision Event was run after a full twelve months of engaging in lean activity. Some lean practitioners would suggest that the EVSA should be the first thing that an organisation should do to ensure that there is an understanding of the approach and buy in from senior figures. Our experience however was that the event was much more effective a year in.

By the time of the EVSA, over two-thirds of the participants had already had direct hands on experience of lean improvement activity. We also had some early results including in particular the significant reductions in trauma mortality which generated interest in the work and gave it credibility. That is not to say that everyone who turned up to the lean vision event did so as an enthusiastic supporter!

The event was run over the space of a week and involved almost sixty people. These were the senior leaders in the organisation, the Board of Directors, the senior medical leaders as well as those from nursing and the allied health professionals. Important partners were also invited such as representatives from the Primary Care Trust, the Patient Forum and the Staff Side Representatives.

At the outset it felt like a high risk event. I didn't know whether people would turn up let alone whether or not they would participate willingly. As it turned out I needn't have worried. Most of the initial concerns and scepticism had melted away by the end of the first day.

By the end of the week we had an enthusiastic sign up to a vision of a lean hospital. That vision centred on clarifying the aims of the hospital and what we were striving to achieve – our 'True North Goals'. This framework is shown below.

Figure 12: What are we trying to achieve?

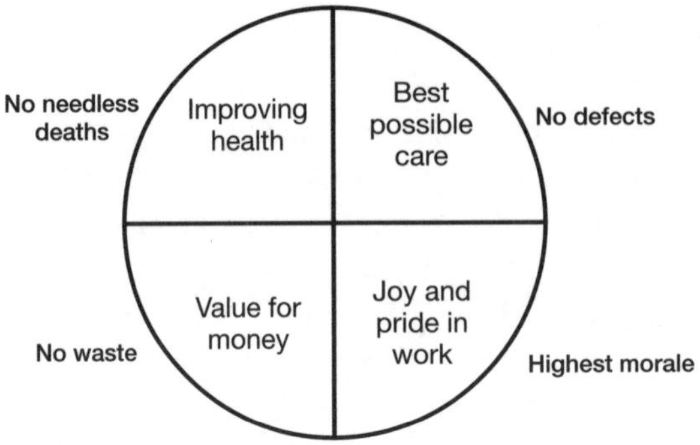

No needless deaths — Improving health — Best possible care — No defects

No waste — Value for money — Joy and pride in work — Highest morale

It was a sobering reflection for everyone to see how far we currently were away from those goals. Our staff surveys showed real problems in some areas with staff satisfaction and morale. In common with other NHS hospitals we knew that our error rates were high with one in ten patients being the subject of some form of adverse event. Although we had made a strong recovery from the financial problems of previous years, we still benchmarked only average for NHS Hospitals in terms of productivity. Finally our mortality rates were significantly higher than the national average and a real cause for concern.

The next part of the vision centred on thinking about the hospital as a collection of patient journeys or valuestreams. This wasn't easy to get our heads around at first but we found that what helped was to think of the hospital as a hierarchy of valuestreams as shown in the diagram below.

Figure 13: Hierarchy of value streams at Bolton Hospitals

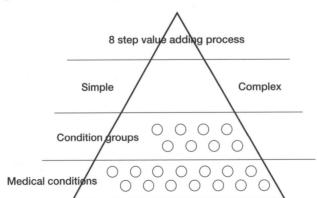

8 step value adding process

Simple — Complex

Condition groups

Medical conditions

The eight-step high-level process describes the way in which value is added to patients who pass through the hospital system. This is shown below and was described in some detail at the beginning of chapter 3.

Figure 14: A healthcare 'valuestream': how value is added

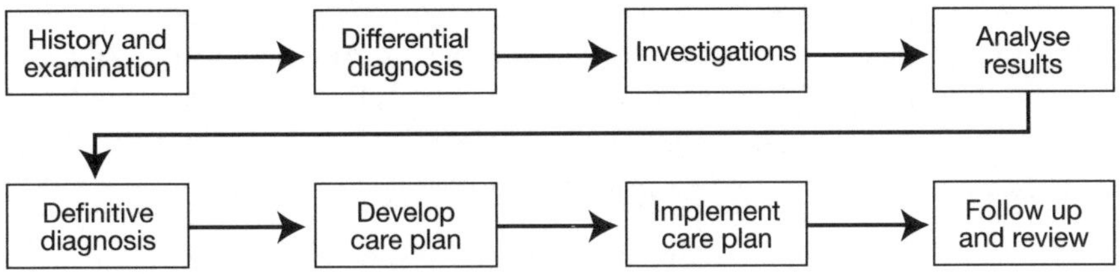

The next categorisation of patient journeys is in to simple and complex. Simple cases are those patients who do not have other complicating co-mobidities; who can largely be dealt with by one specialty or medical discipline; who are only likely to require a relatively short stay in hospital; and who do not need the involvement of other agencies such as social care services.

Complex case patients are the converse of this. Often elderly they have other complicating co-mobidities for example a patient with a hip fracture might also have respiratory problems or a heart condition. They require effective multidisciplinary team-working and close co-operation with other agencies outside the hospital.

The next level in the hierarchy of valuestreams is that of the various condition groups into which patients can be categorised. We made an effort to avoid relating these simply to medical specialties as particular patient journeys may require a combination of professional disciplines to be involved.

Examples of the condition groups included heart and chest, musculoskeletal, abdominal, eyes, head and neck, women's care and children's care. Each of these may have a simple or a complex aspect to them.

During the Lean Vision Event we agreed a number of design principles for the lean hospital of the future. These are shown below:

Design principles for a lean hospital
- Senior decision makers and diagnostics should be located at the front end of the process to get an accurate diagnosis and treatment plan as quickly as possible;

- Patients should be streamed in to simple and complex categories at the outset;

- Patient's development should be monitored closely and there must be the ability to switch between the simple and complex streams should a patient improve or deteriorate;

- Condition based work teams should be created and simple patients placed into flow. This would involve reducing batch sizes, identifying flow stoppers, relocating diagnostics in to the flow, creating standard work and enforcing it, establishing pull systems and setting up visual management. In effect this was the creation of lean healthcare work cells as described earlier in this chapter;

- For complex patients the challenge is different. This is to create 'one decision flow' i.e. to strengthen multi-disciplinary team working and to ensure that the right clinical decision makers co-operate to develop and implement the most effective treatment plan. Where possible the different disciplines should be co-located and intensive support provided to the most complex groups of patients;

- Evidence based clinically effective practice should form the basis for standard work to be followed consistently by professionals throughout the hospital.

Reaching consensus on this set of design principles felt like a major achievement. It was certainly a long way from where we started at the outset of the week. Nevertheless, all it really represented was an agreement about theory. The practical implementation was the challenging next step.

We recognised that this could only be done patient journey by patient journey. The redesign of the trauma journey had shown how the application of lean principles could improve quality, reduce mortality and enhance job satisfaction whilst at the same time lowering costs. Our goal was to do this for all patient groups across the hospital journey by journey.

Our aim following the Lean Vision Event was to begin work straight away on four new journeys; two for simpler groups of patients – cataracts and joint replacements and two for those with complex conditions – abdominal problems and strokes.

We also recognised that some significant changes to the hospital's infrastructure would be needed if we were to become a lean hospital. This included changes to the physical layout.

The hospital had grown up in a haphazard fashion over many years and was a 'hotch potch' of old and modern buildings. Almost nothing is in the right place! An excellent example is that of our children's services. Children's Outpatients are at one end of the site, we have two children's wards 200 meters apart and the neonatal intensive care unit is at the opposite end of the site from the outpatient department next to the maternity unit. This means we have extremely fit paediatricians as during a working day they can walk many miles between the various locations in which sick children are to be found!

It is debatable whether or not the plan to become a lean hospital is the Estates Department's worst nightmare or their every dream come true! The hospital is now committed to spending its capital year on year over a five year period to progressively co-locate interdependent services and to create environments which are suitable for establishing flow.

One good example of this is the issue of radiology. Radiology departments are hospitals' 'monuments'. They are large, centralised departments containing expensive capital equipment such as CT scanners and MR scanners through which many patients with different presenting conditions need to pass. Often they create a classic process bottleneck with batches and queues of patients forming behind the department either in waiting rooms or lying in beds on wards.

The Lean Vision Event established a commitment to take a lean approach to radiology and to relocate diagnostic equipment in to the flow. This means moving the xray machines in to the orthopaedic unit, ultrasound scanners in to the abdominal pain area, ensuring that there is a CT scanner dedicated for stroke patients and so on. It is a large scale and expensive undertaking which will not be achieved quickly.

The traditional way of thinking about hospitals would be to point optimise the radiology department ensuring that equipment and radiology staff are always fully utilised and kept busy even if this kept patients waiting. This needs to be replaced by an understanding that it may be worth allocating more resources to radiology even though this appears to be inefficient if this can bring about quicker diagnosis, better treatment and reduced length of stay, hence improving the overall efficiency of the patient journey as a whole.

These changes to the physical infrastructure are important and not easy to achieve. Of even greater importance and even more difficult however, are the changes to attitudes and daily behaviours that will be required from all members of staff within a lean hospital. This issue is explored in much greater depth in Section Three of this book.

Of course from the patient's point of view the hospital is only a part of their overall healthcare experience. Indeed the vast majority of interactions with healthcare professionals take place outside of hospitals with primary care practitioners and community services. So how would an entire lean healthcare system operate?

The lean healthcare system

If we return to our example of the trauma patient we followed through the hospital earlier we can begin to see that the hospital itself is only a part of the story. The elderly patient who arrives by ambulance in the A&E department having fractured his/her hip in a fall is likely to have had a significant previous history.

Such a patient may have already been under the care of their general practitioner and receiving home nursing and social care support. Alternatively he/she could have been in a residential or nursing home environment. The ambulance service themselves are the first part of the acute episode after a fracture has taken place and the paramedics can initiate some treatments and investigations before the patient even arrives at the hospital. The after hospital element of the patient journey is also critical to the patient's chances of successful recovery and rehabilitation. This will include again the attentions of the general practitioner and district nurse, a range of social services support and may also involve therapists and other community health professionals.

The challenge in a lean healthcare system is to get each element of that wider system no matter which agency the staff are employed by, to be designed on lean principles and organised for whole system flow. This is a considerable challenge! It took Toyota themselves many many years to reach beyond the boundary of their own factories. The Toyota Production System was well developed before Toyota began to extend it back up stream and educate their suppliers in a lean approach.

Nevertheless this whole system approach to lean healthcare is beginning to develop in some places. Indeed in Bolton, the Bolton Primary Care Trust's provider services have been applying lean to a range of community health services with some considerable success. The PCT and the Hospital have been working together using a lean framework to redesign flows across the entire healthcare system to support the NHS target of no patients waiting longer than 18 weeks from referral from their GP to the beginning of their definitive treatment.

An analysis of the current system showed that patients were attending multiple outpatient visits. Furthermore, diagnostics were not fully aligned with outpatient services requiring still further visits to the hospital with more waits and delays. In total the outpatient process was taking as much as 60% of the patients total journey time, even though it was only the diagnostic phase and the actual amount of value added time for the patient was small. The analysis also showed that there were numerous patients on waiting lists for surgery who were not fit for their operations and who needed their health optimising first. Waste and inefficiencies abounded throughout the patient journey for planned treatment for these conditions.

As a result Bolton PCT developed an approach known as CATS, the Clinical Assessment and Treatment Service. This sought to co-locate specialist assessment and diagnostics in a 'one stop shop'. It enabled the completion of the diagnostic element of the patient journey which had previously taken many months within just four weeks. At the same time the hospital has been using lean principles to maximise theatre throughput and reduce waiting times for surgery. Booking systems identify the next available slot for an operation so that patients can be pulled from the waiting list in chronological order as soon as preoperative assessment has shown them to be fit for surgery.

Bolton PCT is currently investing in six primary care resource centres each to cover a population of around 50,000 patients. These will be capable of delivering the CATS type service with specialist assessment and diagnostics much closer to where patients live, thereby reducing the unnecessary cost and difficulty of transport to the hospital and freeing the hospital to spend more time on the more seriously ill patients.

Basing this reconfiguration of the health economy along lean lines – ensuring a smooth flow of patients, good co-ordination between the different agencies and professions and a standardised approach to delivering effective practice – offers the best chance of these changes and investments delivering the maximum benefit both to patients and taxpayers.

Where have we got to?

The first section of this book has:

*   Explored the basic ideas behind a lean approach;
*   Described the challenges and opportunities of applying lean to healthcare;
*   Given a glimpse of what might be expected in a lean ward, clinic or department, a lean patient journey, a whole lean hospital or an entire lean healthcare system.

Unfortunately understanding the theory is the easy part! Doing it in practice is not always so straightforward. The second section of the book takes up this challenge and offers some insights on how to get started on your lean journey in healthcare.

References

1. Institute of Medicine (2001) *Crossing the Quality Chasm*, Washington: National Academy Press.
2. *Health Service Journal* (HSJ) Supplement (19 April 2007), Productive Ward: Releasing Time to Care.

Section Two

How to get started

Section Two of this book is intended as a practical guide for anyone who wants to get started on their own lean healthcare transformation. I hope it will be of use whether you are setting out to improve a clinic, department or office or whether you are more ambitious and seeking to transform a whole hospital or even an entire healthcare system.

The next five chapters describe the Bolton Improving Care System. This is the model that has been developed within Bolton Hospitals with the support of Simpler Consulting to adapt lean methods into a healthcare environment.

Chapter Five provides an overview of the Bolton Improving Care System. Chapters Six, Seven, Eight and Nine then explore the four constituent elements of the BICS cycle: Understanding Value, Learning to See, Redesigning Care, Delivering Benefit.

These chapters contain many practical examples of lean healthcare in action. They also provide some tips on getting started. A case study on the redesign of the journey for patients with fractured hips runs throughout this section to help bring to life how these tools and approaches can be put in to practice.

Unfortunately this section doesn't have all of the answers! Lean Healthcare is a discipline which is still in its infancy. There is more to be learned and understood every day. Hopefully this section will stimulate more lean healthcare pioneers to add to the body of knowledge that is already in place.

Chapter Five

The Bolton Improving Care System

SUMMARY

- **Achieving a successful lean transformation is not about one off initiatives; it requires a sustained systemic approach;**

- **The Bolton Improving Care System (BICS) is a model for applying a lean approach to healthcare which can be used at a variety of levels – departmental, patient journey, hospital wide, or whole health economy;**

- **BICS has the following steps:**
  - **Understanding value**
  - **Learning to see**
  - **Redesigning care**
  - **Delivering benefit;**

- **It needs to be underpinned by the development of skills and capabilities, the handling of employee relations issues, a lean re-orientation of support functions, and a new approach to management and leadership;**

- **Valuestream Analysis Events (VSAs) and Rapid Improvement Events (RIEs) are a powerful means of engaging staff in the lean redesign process.**

Over the last two years, I have attended lots of seminars about lean transformation. I have heard many presentations by hard-nosed manufacturers and financiers extolling the benefits which lean has brought to their organisations. They almost always begin by talking about the application of tools and techniques, valuestream maps, error proofing, just in time systems, but they almost all quickly move on to talking about people – culture, attitudes and behaviours.

The message is clear – just applying lean tools won't make you like Toyota. You need to make lean your own. It needs to become embedded within the culture and a part of daily activity, 'how we do things around here'. Many management consultancies will urge you to avoid 'reinventing the wheel'. They will suggest that they have an off the shelf package of lean tools which you can apply in a straightforward manner. My own view is that what is needed is something a little different.

There is certainly no sense in ignoring the lessons that others have learned. Indeed there is a great deal to be gained by studying experience from other lean transformations and blending it in to your own approach. This can speed up the process of a successful lean implementation. But what has worked well elsewhere can not be applied unthinkingly and without any adaptation for local circumstances. Perhaps the best way to think about what we need is to say we are looking for 'assisted wheel reinvention!'

Developing your own version of the Toyota Production System will require you to do three things:

1. **Adapt creatively** – you need to keep the essentials which make the Toyota system such a success such as recognising the importance of flow and developing a rigorous approach to problem-solving. But you need to place the emphasis where it makes most sense for your own business. For example, in healthcare, reducing batching and queues tackles a very obvious problem; it is much harder to see the immediate relevance of techniques for achieving rapid machine changeovers.

   It is also essential to put the ideas in to your own style and language. 'Best Possible Care' works better in a hospital setting than 'customer satisfaction' and there are many aspects of lean terminology which involve manufacturing terms or even Japanese words which need to be translated in to healthcare speak.

2. **Develop a systematic approach** – this will ensure a consistent application of lean methods and promotes their more rapid spread throughout the organisation. Standard ways of working are needed in terms of the types of improvement activity carried out, the tools that are used and the measurement of results.

3. **Train your staff in your own version of lean** – this creates a sense of ownership and pride in your own organisations' lean system. This can then be deepened through repeated involvement in improvement activity and the momentum built through the publicity given to the achievements secured.

At Bolton Hospital our reinvention of lean has taken the form of the Bolton Improving Care System known as BICS. This is summed up in the diagram opposite.

Understanding value

One of the key principles of a lean approach is to identify and eliminate waste. This can only be done if there is clarity about what is and isn't value adding activity. It is dangerous in the extreme to seek to determine value without fully understanding the customers' needs and wishes. After all it is their money that is paying for the goods or services and in healthcare terms their wellbeing and livelihood that is at stake. BICS employs a variety of tools and techniques to understand the needs and wishes of patients and their carers.

Figure 15: The Bolton Improving Care System (BICS)

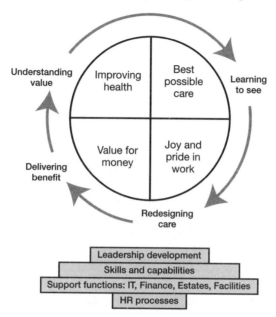

Learning to see

It is amazing how blind we can become in our day to day work to the errors and problems that exist all around us. I was recently taken by one of our matrons on a tour of a busy assessment ward. She was anxious to point out to me some of the accumulated dirt and damage which had come from the wear and tear on one of the busiest parts of the hospital. I had visited that ward a dozen times in the previous year but had not noticed how bad a state things had reached.

We are often so preoccupied with demands of our job that we stop seeing the service through the eyes of the customer – in this case patients and relatives. Learning to see the service as they see it is critical to identifying the opportunities for improvement. This also involves seeking out the hidden processes, for example the movement of medical records, the provision of goods and supplies, which can cause waste and delays but which are rarely immediately apparent to those involved in the direct delivery of care.

Redesigning care

This is the real value added part of the process! It requires innovation and creativity to envision a better way of doing things and to see how this can be brought about. At this phase, BICS aims to embed the lean principles described in Chapter 4. It also aims to work on the following triangle:

Figure 16: Redesign triangle

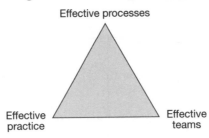

Simple redesign challenges such as reorganising the stockroom on a ward can be achieved in a single day. More complicated redesign efforts such as transforming the whole pathway for stroke patients will take many months. All should seek to address the lean redesign triangle and to be founded on lean principles.

Delivering benefit

This is where a great deal of improvement activity falls down. There are often many good ideas and great enthusiasm but initial achievements are not sustained and the full potential is never realised. This part of the BICS cycle requires a systematic approach to following up what was planned and demands the full ownership and involvement of line managers to move from a one off experiment to a changed way of working every day.

The way in which BICS tackles these four phases, the tools and techniques that are used and some tips on what to do and what to avoid are set out in Chapters Six, Seven, Eight and Nine.

Underpinning the BICS approach is an emergent new way of managing the hospital as a whole. This involves changing the style of management and leadership, developing the right kind of skills and capabilities amongst staff, handling difficult employee relations issues that may be created and re-orientating support functions on to a lean basis. These issues are considered in more depth in Chapter Eleven.

It is worth at this point also commenting on two of the important vehicles that have been used to carry out BICS activity within Bolton. These are the Valuestream Analysis Event or VSA and Rapid Improvement Event or RIE.

It is certainly not the case that lean methodology can only applied through improvement events (sometimes known as Kaizen events). There are many other things that also need to be done. An effective improvement plan will identify major projects that aren't capable of being addressed using an event methodology and also a series of much smaller actions than can be regarded as 'just do its'.

Nevertheless event weeks are an extremely powerful tool. Not only do they achieve things in a much shorter space of time than a traditional committee or working party approach; they are also a powerful organisational development intervention. During the weeks it is heartening to see how the attitudes and behaviours of often sceptical staff shift towards commitment and enthusiasm. Toyota view their own Kaizen events as a way of ensuring that all employees retain the skills and the mindset necessary for the maintenance of the Toyota Production System. In Bolton they have been a way of putting BICS on the map and of achieving the rapid immersion of staff in this new approach.

The valuestream analysis event

The aim of the VSA is to move through the first three phases of the BICS cycle; understanding value, learning to see and redesigning care to come up with a robust improvement plan. As a consequence the VSA lends itself best to transforming whole patient journeys and successful VSAs have been held in Bolton in trauma, stroke care, cataracts and joint replacements.

The VSA approach need not necessarily be restricted just to a patient journey. The Diagnostics and Therapies Division conducted a VSA to come up with a vision and plan for the future of diagnostic and therapy services in the hospital to which all staff could sign up. More latterly therapy staff have themselves conducted their own VSA which has set out a goal of moving therapy services on to a 24 hour, seven day a week basis to support the overall move towards a lean hospital.

VSAs can involve anything from as few as eight staff to as many as thirty. The best results are obtained with twelve to fifteen participants. As a rule of thumb it is helpful if at least a third or more staff are directly involved in delivering the processes in question. A further third may be customers or suppliers to the process and a third again 'fresh eyes'. These bring an outside perspective either from elsewhere in the hospital, from a partner organisation such as the Primary Care Trust or they may be patients or carers.

The VSA maps the current state, develops the vision for an ideal state and then moves towards the creation of a plan for a future state which can be implemented over the coming months. More detail on how to run a VSA is given in Chapter Seven.

The rapid improvement event

The clue is in the name! A rapid improvement event aims to implement a successful change within a single week. The make up of the event team is not dissimilar to that of a VSA although the exact composition will vary depending on the problem in hand. To be successful, an RIE requires a clear definition of the problem and gives staff free rein to experiment and try out new approaches with a view to moving quickly towards implementation of the chosen solution. Rapid improvement events can be done as Point Kaizen activity ie simply to fix one particular problem that has arisen within a given department. Alternatively they may be just one in a series of events that make up the improvement plan for a whole patient journey. There will be more discussion on how to run a rapid improvement event in Chapter Eight.

The key to both a VSA and an RIE lies in the preparation and follow up. In Bolton we operate on a seven week cycle with three weeks preparation, one week events and three weeks of follow up. Not all events are successful and there is a great deal of opportunity cost involved if an event doesn't deliver the desired results. So the preparation and follow up are critical elements. Before we move in to how to get started on implementing the BICS cycle it is also worth saying a word or two about preparing the ground.

Preparing the ground

It is perfectly possible to start your journey by leaping straight in to a valuestream analysis event or even doing Point Kaizen through a rapid improvement event. Alternatively, some organisations begin with an enterprise wide valuestream analysis event or lean vision conference. There is no one right way.

In Bolton, we found that preparing the ground was a valuable first step. Before we ran our first VSA event in August 2005 we had spent many months looking at the general concepts and ideas that lay behind a lean approach. We were also fortunate in being able to visit other organisations that had undergone lean transformations and these visits have continued throughout our journey. We are particularly indebted to BAE Systems, the Royal Navy and the Royal Airforce, Markham Systems and Unipart for allowing us to visit them and for sharing their experience of their own lean transformations.

Attendance at courses and conferences was also helpful. This included specialist healthcare events such as those organised by the Health Service Journal, NHS Confederation or National Institute of Innovation and Improvement and also more general lean events such as those arranged by the Manufacturing Advisory Service. Support and guidance from expert lean practitioners was invaluable, including Dan Jones and his colleagues at the Lean Enterprise Academy and Simpler Consulting, who we have appointed as our strategic consulting partners to support Bolton's lean transformation.

We also organised talks and master classes on various aspects of quality improvement which went beyond lean methodology on topics such as Statistical Process Control, the NHS Modernisation Agency's High Impact Changes, Clinical Engagement and Change Management. This meant that by the time of our initial lean events in the summer of 2005, there was awareness within the organisation of what the approach could offer. Whilst this pre-work isn't essential you may want to think about the best way of preparing the ground before embarking on your own lean journey. That journey begins with a deeper understanding of the needs and wishes of the most important person in any lean healthcare system – the patient.

Over the next four chapters we will explore in more depth the steps in the Bolton Improving Care Cycle. The following case study will provide a real life example of each stage in the process …

Case study: Fractured hip patient journey

The patient journey for those who came through the hospital with serious trauma, in particular fractured hips, was chosen as the first end to end 'valuestream' to be redesigned in Bolton. This was because it was a service giving serious cause for concern.

Bolton has over 1500 admissions for complex fractures each year as it is a large and busy emergency hospital. Almost half of these patients are over 65 and many have complicating co-mobidities. Those patients with fractured hips were a particularly high risk group.

The relative adjusted risk mortality in Bolton in 2004/5 from a fractured hip was 173.9. The average for NHS hospitals is 100. As can be seen this is a high level of potentially avoidable mortality.

Not surprisingly this situation affected the morale of staff within the department. Many attempts have been made over the years to bring about improvements using traditional healthcare approaches involving clinical audit, the application of research and development findings and experimenting with a variety of 'good ideas' suggested by a variety of clinicians.

None of these had succeeded in tackling the worryingly high levels of excess mortality. As a consequence, this patient journey was chosen as a topic for lean redesign with the aim of reducing the patient's journey time, improving the quality of the patients experience and satisfaction of staff and tackling the worryingly high mortality rates.

What was actually done and the results that were obtained will be set out in each of the following four chapters.

Chapter Six

Understanding value

SUMMARY

- Healthcare professionals often think they know what patients need; this isn't always the same as the patients' own view!

- Value in healthcare is created by
  - Technical efficiency: how well the processes are designed and operated
  - The aesthetic of the experience: both human and environmental

- Quantitative analysis can reveal surprising facts about the characteristics of the patient groups served;

- There are a range of qualitative research tools which can be used to understand the views of patients and carers;

- Innovative approaches to involving patients in co-designing services hold great promise.

The starting point of any lean improvement activity whether in a single department or for an entire healthcare system is to understand value from the point of view of the customer ie the patient and their family or carers. The continual elimination of waste is a primary component of a lean approach but this can only be achieved if we can easily distinguish what is waste and what is value adding activity. Healthcare professionals often believe that they know what the patient needs. Many doctors and nurses will say to me 'but we spend all day talking to patients, of course we understand what needs to be done for them'. Unfortunately delivering care is not the same as receiving it.

A recent article in the *British Medical Journal* contained a prescription for reintroducing dignity into medical care. It contained a quote from the late Anatole Broyard, the former editor of the New York Times book review. Broyard wrote in a moving way about the challenges he experienced when facing metastasic prostate cancer 'to the typical physician' he wrote 'my illness is a routine incident in his rounds, while for me it is the crisis of my life. I would feel better if I had a doctor who at least perceived this incongruity. I just wish he would give me his whole mind just once, be bonded with me for a brief space, survey my soul as well as my flesh to get at my illness. For each man is ill in his own way'. To put it more prosaically an elderly female patient recently recounted an incident where a doctor asked her to strip to her waist and lie on the couch. 'Don't worry' he said 'I do this every day'. 'Yes' she replied 'but I don't'.

The insight from this is that understanding the patient's experience can not simply be a question of counting the process steps and identifying disruptions to the flow or opportunities for error. Paul Bate and Glenn Robert have suggested that the value that is added to the patient in a healthcare interaction is of two types (2). Firstly the effectiveness and efficiency with which the process is conducted. Secondly, the aesthetics of the experience – both human and physical.

The **technical efficiency** is determined by the skill and professionalism of the professionals involved and the adequacy with which the systems of care are designed. This determines the outcome from the patient's point of view and the cost from the providers perspective.

Equally important however is the **experience** of the patient as he or she moves along his or her journey. This can again be determined by the design of the process which will determine whether or not the patient has to wait, how far he or she has to travel and so on. It is however also critically influenced by the quality of the physical environment – is it clean, welcoming and healing – and by the quality of the human interactions.

Bate and Robert's research at Luton and Dunstable Hospital showed that patient journeys have a number of 'critical moments' that have an unduly large influence on what the patient feels about the treatment he or she has received. These include, for example, the initial reception, the explanation of the diagnosis, the breaking of bad news, the quality of information provided and the support to make decisions. This may be thought of as the **'aesthetics'** of the valuestream.

The challenge is to understand the patient's wants and needs both in terms of the technical efficiency and effectiveness of their care and its human and environmental aesthetics.

Achieving a better understanding of what commercial companies would call your customer base can be done in two ways; quantitative analysis and qualitative research.

Quantitative analysis

A good starting point when embarking on a lean redesign of a department or of a service is to ask the question 'Where do our patients come from and what are their major characteristics'? A great deal can be gained from an analysis of information contained on the hospital's patient administration system or in the patient's casenotes. Important questions to ask might be:

- What is the demand on our service by hour of the day, day of the week and month of the year?
- How are patients referred in to our service? Is it through a general practitioner, as an emergency or by a specialist referral from another service?
- What are the characteristics of our patient population? What is the mix of gender, age, social class and ethnicity.
- What are the most common conditions which present to our service? A simple statistical analysis can be undertaken to identify the most commonly occurring conditions.

Often these questions throw up some interesting results. For example, analysis showed that a high proportion of patients attending the emergency department are from the socially and economically most deprived wards in the town and that these patients also have the lowest uptake of planned procedures. This indicated an urgent need to work with the primary and community care providers in those electoral wards to tackle current need at a local level. An analysis of the ophthalmology service in Bolton showed that 84% of the work of the department was made up of straight-forward cataract operations. This came as something as a surprise to the ophthalmology team who focused a lot of their effort and energy in to the much smaller number of more complex conditions. They concluded that it was important to manage those simple cataracts more efficiently to leave more time to be dedicated to the less high volume but more difficult to resolve complex problems.

Ideally this kind of quantitative analysis should precede any lean improvement activity. Whilst it can be carried out during an improvement event itself this is far from ideal and takes time away from other activities. The three week preparation time for a valuestream analysis event or rapid improvement event is the right point to ask these kinds of questions of the data. This means that the team can start the event with a briefing about the main characteristics of their patient population.

Qualitative research techniques

As well as the hard numbers it is important to get a flavour of patients' actual opinions and views. A range of qualitative research techniques exist, many of which are regularly used by commercial companies as part of their customer research. It is important that these are properly used and interpreted if misleading results are to be avoided. There is always the risk that surveys and questionnaires can be used to validate professionals own opinions of their service. Questions such as 'How grateful do you feel to the nursing staff?' are probably best avoided!

There are a number of useful sources of advice in relation to qualitative research. The NHS Modernisation Agency produced a variety of guides, many of which can still be obtained from its successor body, the National Institute of Innovation and Improvement. Other organisations such as the Picker Institute can also be of help. The most commonly used approaches are detailed below.

1. Questionnaires

These can range from short comment cards with only a few questions which are given to patients at the end of their inpatient stay, to much more thorough and detailed examples such as the NHS National Patient Survey. Care should be taken in using survey methods to make sure that a representative sample of patients is surveyed. This should be reflective of the whole population mix covering different genders, ages, social and ethnic backgrounds. It is also important to ensure that the questions are structured in such a way that will avoid bias or leading the respondent towards a particular desired answer.

Written surveys are less effective in seeking the views of those who are illiterate, who do not read English, who can not use their hands or who have impaired eye sight. It is also true that a number of people have neither the time nor the inclination to fill out questionnaires. Often therefore the responses are bi-polar in nature ie only the very satisfied or the very dissatisfied bother to respond. Nevertheless providing that a large enough sample is taken and that that sample is properly constructed, then a well designed questionnaire can provide valuable evidence as to patients' views.

2. Focus groups

This is another commonly used market research technique. Again it is essential that the focus group is properly constructed and is a representative cross sample of the patient population under consideration. Care should be taken to organise a non-threatening venue in which patients can relax and give of their opinions freely. I have sat in on a number of focus groups that have produced rich discussions and revealed a great deal of detail about patients' views. They are particularly effective when patients are asked to describe their actual experiences rather than simply answering questions as to whether or not they are satisfied.

A difficulty with focus groups lies in the interpretation of results as they will almost inevitably be a range of conflicting opinions and views about the services. One of the challenges in understanding value from the customers' point of view is to recognise that each customer is an individual. The aim in a lean healthcare design process must be to cater for the whole range of wants and needs and not simply to develop a service that will meet the average of everyone's expectations. Indeed, this runs the risk of satisfying no-one!

3. Interviews

This can be a valuable way of exploring in depth the experience of a single individual. The NHS Modernisation Agency termed these 'discovery interviews' and explored them in depth with cardiac patients (3). An immense amount of learning is possible about what is good and bad about a service and about what patients would like to see improved by using this interview methodology.

The drawback is that it represents a small sample size unless the time is available to conduct a large number of interviews which is rarely the case. One of the most significant benefits of using the interview methodology is the opportunity it can provide for a senior manager or clinician responsible for a service to engage directly with those people he or she serves. This creates an emotional engagement with the issues that simply can not be derived from a mere consideration of statistical analysis or through reading summaries of interviews conducted by others.

4. Observations of care

These are quite often used within the nursing profession. To some extent they are the healthcare equivalent of 'Ohno's Circle'! They involve the observer sitting in a place where care is delivered in an unobtrusive way, often for two to three hours at a stretch making careful notes about what they can see. In Bolton, the executive team have all conducted observations of care on our wards and in clinics. This has been a revealing experience which shows plainly some excellent examples of wonderful care, but sadly also examples of where we do not get it right.

5. Patient diaries

This is a real time version of the interview! Again a great deal of useful insights can be gained by asking patients to record what happens to them throughout their healthcare journey. This can be more effective than a patient looking back on the experience during an interview as they may well not recall important incidents and examples, either of positives which can be built upon, or failings in care which need to be tackled. Again the approach suffers from being restricted to a small sample size and also to those patients who are confident and literate or articulate enough to produce an account of their experience.

6. Complaints

These do provide insights in to the patient's experience. A genuine learning organisation treats complaints as opportunities for improvement, drilling down to the root causes and ensuring that action is taken to prevent a reoccurrence. However they clearly represent a skewed sample ie those occasions where things went sufficiently far wrong for the patient to feel compelled to complain. They are also information about a negative outcome, i.e. what the patient's do not want to happen to them rather than what they do!

7. Patient associations, groups and forums

There are a great many different types of organisations in which patients are involved. It is useful to distinguish between organisations of patients and those for patients. The first category is usually made up of patients who have had first hand experience of a particular service, whilst the latter is more often made up of relatives, carers and compassionate third parties who want to advocate on patients behalf or raise funds for a particular service.

It is likely that the distribution of people within such groups will again be bi-polar ie the very satisfied and the very dissatisfied. Those who have had a 'average' experience may be unlikely to join up. Nevertheless such groups often spend a considerable amount of time reflecting upon their collective experiences and developing ideas about improvements that are needed in a service. They can, therefore, be a rich source of advice and inspiration.

As with quantitative analysis it is better if these tools are used well ahead of the start of a lean redesign process. Indeed it can be argued that they should be used on a continual basis as a matter of good practice so that the healthcare organisation always understands how well it is meeting the needs and wishes of its customers. However, some use of these techniques to involve patients during either a valuestream analysis event or rapid improvement event can be highly beneficial.

This is particularly so if this is done to validate or add to previously generated data on patients' experiences and wishes. Engaging patients directly through observations, interview and discussion during an event week, emphasises to those staff involved the importance of what they are doing and grounds it in the reality of patients' day to day experience. It appeals to the emotions as well as the intellect and reinforces that the overriding aim of the lean effort is the improvement of care for the patient.

During a valuestream analysis event to redesign the stroke services in Bolton, a senior manager, nurse and doctor returned to the Trust having met with Jigsaw who are the local support group for stroke patients. The three of them were humbled by the experience. The passion, concern and innovative suggestions made by the group had moved them deeply. What's more they had just spent a number of days analysing the process of care for stroke patients in some detail and understood the flaws, errors and problems within it. The senior nurse commented 'We received a round of applause at the end from the group which we didn't really feel that we deserved. We simply can't afford to let this group of patients down'.

Pulling it all together

Having generated a range of hard and soft information about your patients, it is necessary to draw some conclusions from it. One useful way of organising the information is to draw a Kano chart. This is a technique used to understand the needs of customers of commercial companies and can easily be translated in to the healthcare setting. The outline of the Kano chart is shown opposite.

As can be seen the Kano chart distinguishes between those basic unspoken requirements that patients would expect to always be present as part of the service through to those delighters that are rarely experienced but would make a real impression if they were provided. Sadly many of the unspoken basic requirements are often absent, such as preventing me from having a medication error or preventing me from getting an infection. Some of the more imaginative delighters such as valet parking won't have a beneficial impact unless the basic requirements and needs of patients are first delivered.

The analysis of patients' wants and needs can be used to create a value statement. This sets out the care requirements and expectations of the customer, ie the patient and should be the first step towards a lean process redesign. An example of a typical value

Figure 17: 'Kano' – tool understand – value

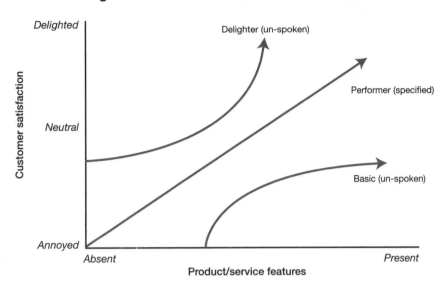

statement drawn up by staff on a day surgery unit might be 'To provide patients with their operations in a timely manner, in pleasant surroundings, delivered by staff who know what they are doing and who care about it, and with the minimum amount of pain or hassle'. This value statement is the standard by which the current state of the service can be measured and a plan drawn up for improvements.

Before concluding this chapter it is worth considering two innovative examples which go beyond simply asking patients their views, to actively involve them in the improvement of services. Interestingly both draw on the principles of design. The first relates to work Bolton Hospital and the Primary Care Trusts' diabetes services has done with the Design Council; the second is the experience based design work piloted by the NHS National Institute for Innovation and Improvement at Luton and Dunstable Hospital.

Reframing diabetes care in Bolton

During 2005, the Design Council led a number of innovative projects to apply the principles and techniques of design to the improvement of public services. One of these projects took place with the diabetes team in Bolton. The Design Council team were not healthcare experts, indeed they had not worked within a healthcare setting before. Their expertise was in using design methodology to allow companies to produce products and services that better suited customers needs.

They conducted a series of interviews and discussion groups with staff and diabetes patients over a number of weeks. From this they built up a model of the motivations, desires and fears of diabetic patients. Compliance with the treatment regime is important to the successful management of a diabetic condition, but is not always easy to achieve which can lead to prolonged bouts of ill health and possibly even hospitalisation. One of the issues which the Design Council team explored therefore was how to enable patients to become more compliant with their treatment regime.

An innovative approach which they developed was the use of a set of playing cards. These cards contained a series of issues or statements which had been worked up from interviews and discussion groups with patients' themselves. The cards presented a variety of statements such as 'I simply can't understand what the doctor is saying to me' or 'I know I should give up smoking but I am struggling with it'. The cards were then used as part of a discussion session with diabetic nurse practitioners and individual patients. They created a dialogue that drew out the patients own needs and concerns rather than an artificial structure imposed upon them by professionals.

As a consequence patients believed that they could develop not only a treatment plan but a life plan for managing their diabetes more effectively. This was much more likely to be followed because of the degree of ownership which they felt for it. Although this work hadn't been conducted from a lean perspective, interestingly it contained many lean themes, including the need to surface hidden problems to reframe existing processes, (in this case the dialogue between professionals and patients), and to develop new approaches through a series of iterative prototypes or experiments.

Experience-based design

A second interesting example is that of the experience based design work conducted at Luton and Dunstable Hospital by the National Institute for Innovation and Improvement mentioned at the beginning of this chapter. This has been extensively researched by Paul Bate and Glenn Robert (4). This again drew on design principles and was based on the notion that there are a number of critical moments, or touch points, during a patient's experience that make a lasting impact on them.

The study worked with head and neck cancer patients and conducted in-depth interviews and diaries of the patient's experiences. The critical moments which were identified included, for example, the looking in the mirror moment, the breaking the bad news moment and the radiotherapy planning moment. The study also used DVD to capture the patient's experiences and reflections on film. It is both moving and powerful to hear patients describe the highs and lows of their journey in compelling terms.

Using the principles of co-design between customer and supplier, the study put groups of patients and professionals together and asked them to work in partnership to improve the management of these critical moments. This involved training for staff in communication skills and also changes to the physical environment. Often small simple things had a huge impact on the patient's experience. One negative issue for example was the clutter of boxes and equipment stored in a room used for breaking bad news, whilst a positive one was the presence of a window with a pleasant view which provided a place for quiet reflection.

Both the Bolton Diabetes work and the Luton and Dunstable work on experience based design show how it is possible to move from treating patients as passive recipients to actively engaging them as full partners in the co-design of services. Within Bolton we routinely now have patients as members of VSA and RIE teams. Clearly in twos and threes they can not be representative of the whole patient community, but their presence keeps staff focused on the ultimate goal of their work which is the improvement of outcomes and experience from the patient's perspective.

Having understood what is and isn't valuable to the patient, we need to be able to judge how far our current service is adequately meeting those patient's needs. To do this we need to learn to see the process as it really is rather than its official version on a nicely printed and laminated flow chart! This is the subject of the next chapter.

Case Study: Understanding value for fractured hip patients

A team was assembled to redesign the patient journey for those with fractured hips which brought together all appropriate expertise including an orthopaedic surgeon, an orthogeriatrician, specialist trauma nurses, physiotherapists, occupational therapists, social care professionals and representatives from theatres, accident & emergency and radiology departments. The Director of Nursing acted as the Executive Sponsor and took a leading role in getting the project off the ground.

The first step was to better understand the customer base and what would be regarded as value. Statistical analysis was done to identify the pattern of admissions by time of day, by day of week and on a seasonal basis. It was also identified that many of these patients were elderly with complicating co-mobidities.

An exercise was then undertaken to understand what was valuable from the patients' and relatives' perspective. This was done by interviewing patients and ex-patients by issuing questionnaires, by tracking patients through the process and observing what happened to them and by having a former patient as a permanent member of the project team. A Kano chart was drawn up to summarise the team's findings about what was valuable to the 'customers'. The main headings of the chart are shown below:

KANO CATEGORIES FOR FRACTURED HIP PATIENTS

Basic unspoken requirements
- Competence of the staff involved
- Expect to be seen in a timely fashion
- Expect a safe, clean environment
- Expect notes and x-rays to arrive appropriately
- Expect a friendly approach from staff

Performer requirements
- Expect to worry less as a result of assessment on admission
- Expect to be seen by a senior doctor
- Expect an interest to be taken and questions on wider health

- Expect the right diagnostic tests and examination
- Be given a chance to ask questions, feel comfortable, safe and reassured

Delighters (these are things which patients don't necessarily expect but which if present would enhance the experience)
- Exceeding expectations in terms of the information and support given
- Honesty about difficult issues and complications e.g. MRSA side-effects
- Easy for relatives to park their cars!

As can be seen from this analysis, sadly even the things which are basic unspoken expectations aren't ones which hospitals always manage to meet. This understanding of what was valuable to patients was used as the basis of the next phase, that of identifying which activities were adding value and which were merely waste. This is described in Chapter Seven.

Checklist for getting started on understanding value

❏ Collect as much data as you can on your patient population. See what you can obtain from the hospital's information department, from the clinical audit team, the complaints or customer relations department and from published reports

❏ Do some simple analysis which will provide you with a picture of where your patients come from and what their major characteristics are

❏ Plan and conduct a series of interventions to seek the views of patients about the service as it currently exists

❏ Make sure that you seek a representative sample and elicit information in a way that is valid and reliable

❏ Develop a way of categorising patients needs and wants that makes sense for your service; produce a value statement that will summarise patients' views and guide you in determining what is of true value and what is only waste

❏ Consider ways in which you can involve patients as full partners in your lean journey rather than as passive recipients of your well meaning questions.

References
1. Cochinov, H.M. (2007) *British Medical Journal*, 28th July, Vol 335, pp 184–187.
2. Bate, P. & Robert, G. (2007) *Bringing User Experience to Healthcare Improvement*, Oxford: Radcliffe Publishing.
3. NHS Modernisation Agency (2003) *A guide to using discovery interviews to improve care*, Department of Health.
3. Bate, P. & Robert, G., ibid.

Chapter Seven

Learning to see*

SUMMARY

- The huge amounts of waste that abound in the healthcare workplace usually go unnoticed;

- Staff can be trained to look through 'lean goggles' to see the waste and then eliminate it;

- Value Stream Analysis events (VSAs) are a powerful means of learning to see the waste and problems within our current processes;

- A successful VSA requires thorough preparation, skilled facilitation and determined follow up;

- The challenge is to make waste and problems visible within day to day work so they can be analysed and addressed.

It was 6.30 on a Tuesday evening. The Consultant Geriatrician and Matron from the Trauma service had had a long and hard day. I chatted to them as they were leaving the seminar room where they had been reporting back on Day 2 of our first ever valuestream analysis event looking at the service which we provided to patients with serious fractures. A team made up mostly of clinical staff had spent the day mapping in detail the patient's journey through the hospital. They had spoken to patients and relatives and understood in greater depth than ever before what actually happened on the ground.

Both the consultant and the matron were visibly moved. The consultant said 'I knew we had a problem but I didn't know it was as bad as this; I just didn't know we were doing this to patients. We have got to change it starting right now'. This is typical of the impact that valuestream analysis events can have. This particular consultant later described it as 'psychologically unsettling'.

Health service staff on the whole are altruistically motivated. They join healthcare as a profession because they want to help others and do good. In their own individual interactions with patients they strive to meet this ideal. Sadly the outcome and the

---

*'Learning to See' is the title of a seminal book by John Shook and Mike Rother on process mapping (1). It is also the name given to the second phase of the BICS cycle.

experience for patients is often far less than the levels of quality to which staff aspire but most of the time staff don't get to see this. They see only what happens in their own sphere of influence. Understanding the whole picture – learning to see it with all of its waste, errors, duplication and potential harm is indeed an unsettling experience. It's also the first and absolutely necessary step on the road to improvement.

Barriers to seeing waste

So why is it so hard for healthcare professionals to see the waste that surrounds them? Firstly, most people only see their own small part of the process. Patient journeys are often incredibly complex involving many different departments and members of staff. But while patients move laterally through the hospital, most staff are fixed in their ward, clinic or department and can see only their own part of the patient's journey. Secondly staff inevitably see the service they deliver through the professional's eyes. As the story in the previous chapter made clear, what is simple and routine for a healthcare professional, might be one of the most traumatic and unnerving life experiences that a patient ever goes through. Thirdly, there are a whole range of hidden processes which hardly anyone ever sees – information flows, the availability of transport, the movement of medical records, the processing of blood samples – all of these are essential elements which can create waste and have the potential for error but which are rarely visible in the day-to-day running of a hospital.

The pod analogy

A good metaphor for these hidden processes can be found in the pod. This is a contraption found in many hospitals. It consists of a series of tubes through which blood samples in specially prepared containers pass powered by compressed air. These tubes link the various parts of the hospital such as the A&E department, wards and clinics with the pathology laboratory. The idea is that blood samples can be quickly moved to the lab and tested with the results sent back via computer.

Hardly anyone ever thinks about the inner workings of the pod system. During a lean event one of our pathology managers remarked that he had worked in the hospital for twenty-five years and had only just realised what a significant part the pod played in the efficiency of his own department. As far as doctors and nurses in the emergency department were concerned, they had completed a task when they had put a blood sample in to the pod, then it was hidden from view. The pathology department may not even know of its existence. There was no easy way of telling whether the pod was working effectively or not, yet breakdowns and delays were an inherent feature of the system. As a result there were many delays and frustrations for which the emergency department, the wards and the pathology laboratory all blamed each other.

The workings of the pod system were a mystery to almost everyone and few even thought of its existence, yet it played a crucial part in determining whether or not the service being delivered was of an acceptable standard. This is a striking metaphor for the vast range of invisible processes that need to work smoothly if the patient's journey is to resemble a lean production line. It is essential that we are able to identify these invisible processes and to understand the inherent waste and potential defects which they embody so that these can be addressed.

Lean goggles

So how can we enable staff to see the waste that surrounds them? You can start by teaching staff about the seven kinds of waste which Tahichi Ohno originally identified. A good way to bring this home to people is to relate it to their everyday experiences as a consumer. The health warning on this is that once you start to put on your lean goggles and look for waste, airports and shopping centres will never seem the same! Our Simpler sensei is a particular fan of waste spotting at airports. As he puts it 'whenever you see shops where there shouldn't really be shops, you know you are in trouble'!

A further health warning is that once staff learn about the seven wastes then any management initiatives are closely scrutinised to discover whether or not they really add value. 'That's not very lean' is a phrase now often heard in Bolton and (it has to be admitted) it's sometimes said ironically. If this is said about a management initiative it often has a ring of truth about it and wise managers would do well to think again about whatever proposal is being described in such terms.

Once staff understand the theory of the seven wastes, then waste spotting can and should become a daily activity. Empowering staff to cut waste providing they can do it safely, for example by eliminating duplication of paperwork or removing unnecessary tasks is liberating in itself and has the added value of freeing up staff time for direct patient care. This form of waste spotting is at its most powerful when it is part of a deliberate lean redesign process. The way that this is being done in Bolton Hospital is through the use of week long valuestream analysis events or VSAs to kick off the redesign of whole patient journeys.

Running a valuestream analysis event (VSA)

The way the VSA has been used in Bolton is as a week-long event. During that week a cross-section of staff work together to look at a particular patient journey, or sometimes at a whole service such as therapy provision. They look in detail at the current state, envision an ideal state (letting their creativity run riot)!, develop a more concrete vision of a future state that should be achievable over the next twelve to eighteen months and finally agree an improvement plan to make it happen.

Here are some basic pointers if you want to run your own VSA event:

Before the event:

1. **Choose the topic for attention** – this could be an issue in a single department, e.g. why do we have long waits in our x-ray rooms or across a whole patient journey e.g. why are our mortality rates high for stroke patients. The aim should be to choose an initiative that is a high priority and a real problem for you. Preferably one where there is a good chance of some early success and certainly one where you know you can enlist at least a few enthusiastic clinicians and line managers to take part.

2. **Select the team** – VSA teams can have anything from eight to thirty people on them but the optimum size is around twelve. The majority of those on the team should come from the work area in question. Others should be 'fresh eyes'. These are people with an interest and commitment but without necessarily having any direct knowledge of the service in question. These might be staff or managers from other parts of the organisation, or even from outside the hospital. It can also be incredibly powerful to have patients and carers themselves as members of the team.

3. **Choose a team leader** – preferably this should be somebody with line management responsibility for making the changes stick. Hierarchy is not necessarily an issue. Indeed one of the powerful spin offs of VSAs is the way that they break down barriers between different groups of staff. Ward managers have often proved to be excellent team leaders, able to coral nurses, consultants and managers alike. Importantly the team leader must have people skills, organisational ability and not panic when under pressure as VSAs can create a highly charged, emotional atmosphere.

4. **Ensure good facilitation and support.** This can come from the local improvement team (the BICS team in Bolton for example), or from an outside consultancy if you are using one.

5. **Identify an Executive sponsor**. We have found this to be useful in Bolton. The Executive Sponsor is a Director or a senior manager or clinician who will have responsibility for this piece of work at Board level. It is their job to clear away any obstacles for the team during the week, to provide them with moral support and, to be present and visible for at least part of the week.

6. **Free the team from all other work**. This is perhaps the biggest challenge, particularly in a hospital environment. It is not easy to free consultant surgeons and anaesthetists from the operating theatre for a whole week, or to keep the ward going with the ward manager and a number of nursing staff away from the job, but the most successful events manage to do this.

   For the staff themselves it can be quite tough. Many put in a long day on a VSA and then finish off their emails in the evening. The high levels of motivation and commitment which these events generate seem to carry people through it but don't underestimate the potential strain.

7. **Brief staff in the areas covered by the VSA**. This is extremely important. It can highly irritating for staff to have to shoulder more of the burden whilst their colleagues are 'away doing lean for a week'. The irritation is further increased if they are plagued by staff with clipboards asking them questions and following patients around their department! Consequently communicating the aims of the event and keeping people briefed as it progresses is absolutely essential. When our Director of Nursing leads such events, she produces a bulletin at the end of each day with the engaging headline 'They've done **what**?'.

8. **Do your pre-event analysis and preparation thoroughly**. It greatly helps if the event starts with basic data about the valuestream/patient journey in question already organised in to an easily understandable format. The work to understand value from the patient's perspective as described in Chapter 6, should also be done ahead of the event, although some engagement with patients and carers during the event week helps to give an added sense of purpose and relevance to the work.

9. **Assemble everything that the team will need**. This needs to include a room in which they can work free of distractions, complete with flipcharts, Post-it notes, felt-tip pens etc. A plentiful supply of coffee and chocolate also helps the proceedings go more smoothly!

During the event

Day one – training, aims, goals

The event should kick-off with a briefing from a senior figure, preferably a Director or the Chief Executive, on the importance of the topic and its relevance to the work of the hospital as a whole. There then follows a classroom based training session over two to three hours to introduce novices to the basics of lean principles including the idea that all work is a process, the seven kinds of waste and the principles of flow, pull, 6S, standard work and visual management. Staff who have been on earlier events can be used to brief those who are complete novices.

The team are also reminded that they will be visiting areas in which staff are working and patients are being cared for and that they need to proceed with sensitivity and tact. This training usually takes the first morning of day 1. The afternoon is taken up by reflecting on the previously collected data about the service and on information about patients' views. From this the team develop a business case 'Why use lean?' and produce a value statement as defined from the patient's viewpoint. Finally the team are encouraged to define measures that will gauge the success of the lean redesign process during the rest of the week.

Day two – mapping the current state

The team often split in to smaller groups and spread out in to the hospital to map the patient's journey. This is done by starting at the point at which the patient leaves the hospital and working backwards through the journey. This feels awkward and unusual at first but is a good way of picking up all of the various branches in the process and the hidden activities which are needed to support it. Useful approaches to understanding the patient journey and describing it are shown in the section on tools that follows this overview of the VSA.

Day three – visioning on ideal state

Depending on the complexity of the journey the current state map often may run over on to Day Three. Once the current state map is finished it's time for some creativity! Some simple innovation exercises can be useful here to move the team out of thinking about their current problems and into being radical about what the service could look like in the future. This visioning of the ideal state is intended to free up thinking. Staff can get extraordinarily imaginative when asked to produce a vision of the service free of any constraints of resources or technology. Whilst this ideal state may never be fully achievable, it allows a break from the past and some ideas from the ideal state almost always find a way in to the future state.

Day four – the future state and the improvement plan

By Day Four the team is encouraged to move back towards reality. They are asked to plan for a definitive future state. This needs to be a dramatic improvement on the current state but should be realisable within the next twelve-month period. The future state takes the imagination and creativity of the ideal state and finds ways in which progress can be made towards this despite the compromises that are necessary given the reality of the starting point.

By the end of Day Four the team should be working on an improvement plan to make the future state a reality. This improvement plan should include:

- **Just do its** – these are simple, straightforward things which can be done with the minimum of fuss and without a great deal of permission.
- **Projects** – these are more significant pieces of work that may require substantial investment or the support of senior management in the organisation. They therefore require more thorough planning or analysis. Examples have included the plan to relocate plain film x-ray machines in to the orthopaedics area, necessitating the purchase of capital equipment.
- **Rapid improvement events (RIE)** – these are a further type of week long events. The emphasis of RIEs is not on planning but on doing. They aim to take an aspect of the future state and make it a reality within a short space of time. RIEs are covered in detail in Chapter Eight.

Day five – the outbrief

The morning of Day Five is spent preparing for an outbrief session. The outbrief session is a report back from the team on what they have achieved and learned during the week. It is a highly important event which is a communications vehicle, and also a celebration of the efforts and ingenuity that has gone in to the week's work. These outbrief events in Bolton are well attended. The Lecture Theatre is often standing room only!

Participants include members of the event team (or teams if more than one event has been run during the week which is often the case); staff from the area in question who are often keen to know what is being recommended for their future; Senior Clinicians and Managers from within the hospital including Non-Executive Directors and the Chair; and interested observers from outside which in the past have included the PCT and Strategic Health Authority. The outbrief events always generate great energy and commitment. As one of my director colleagues has said in the past 'If only we could bottle this, we would make a fortune'.

After the event: follow up

One of the saddest and most frustrating things is when an excellent VSA or RIE is inadequately followed up. The energy, momentum and enthusiasm generated during the week-long event can quickly turn in to cynicism unless the promised actions are delivered. Consequently the follow up phase is of great significance.

The improvement plan for the VSA should include individual accountabilities and timelines. It is the job of the team leader and Executive Sponsor to ensure that follow up happens, prompted and supported by the facilitator from the improvement team. There is a formal 30 day follow up which in Bolton is reported to the Executive Board (made up of Directors and Senior Clinicians). There is also a 90 day follow up where the Chief Executive reviews with a core team from the event the progress that has been made.

Other actions to be taken after the event include publicising the outcomes and making sure that all members of staff in the areas affected understand why change is being proposed and what it will mean for them. The most powerful way of doing this is to use those staff who have been involved in the event as the key communicators.

Another issue after the event is to follow up on individuals who have been on teams. They have often become enthusiastic advocates for a lean approach and may be keen to take part in further activity. Indeed one of the important spin-offs of this work is that it is a great vehicle for talent management, ie for spotting and nurturing the leaders of the future.

Tools that are useful on a VSA

The starting point of the VSA is understanding of value from the customer's perspective. Tools that are useful in achieving this were described in some detail in Chapter Six. The following are tools that can help in learning to see:

Valuestream map

This can be done in varying degrees of detail depending on the scale and complexity of the valuestream involved. The process should be mapped backwards from the point of the patient's exit from the system. As a minimum the patient flow through the process should be mapped together with the supporting information flows. Sometimes it might also be helpful to map the flow of materials and the presence of clinical decision makers at key points of the process.

Having developed a map which everyone can agree is a fair reflection of the process, staff can begin the job of identifying which steps in the process are value-added, which are non-value-added but currently unavoidable and which are simply waste. The realisation of how much waste there is in our processes is often a sobering revelation!

Other measures which can be gleaned from the valuestream map are the touch time (the amount of time staff are actually in contact with patients) as opposed to the flow time (the total amount of time which a process takes including waiting); the takt time or pulse, this is the frequency cycle for particular activities, for example the rate at which operations need to be done in theatre to achieve a certain throughput; the yield, this is the percentage chance of a patient passing through every step in the process in a completely error free way. Again this is often a sobering statistic! The levels of waste and potential for error in healthcare processes are so high that yields are often calculated by staff at less than 1%.

Patient and staff perceptions

Interviews and surveys are often used to check the perceptions of staff and patients at particular points in the process. Post-it notes with smiley or frowny faces are used to indicate how staff and patients are feeling at a given time. Interestingly these don't always coincide. There are times when both patients and staff are unhappy but also times where there is a mismatch between the two. The more sophisticated form of this analysis is the identification of critical moments or touch points as described from the work at Luton and Dunstable in Chapter Six.

Spaghetti diagrams

These show how far staff or patients move in a particular service. Again these are highly illuminating. One of our surgeons noted that 'we walk miles simply to find out where the poorly patients are'. An example of a typical spaghetti diagram is shown below:

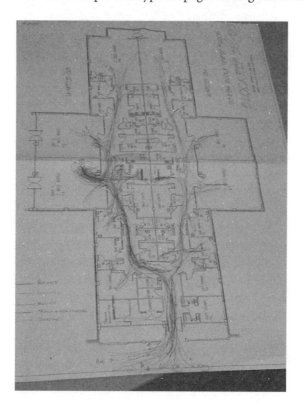

Hand off charts

Another useful tool is the hand off chart. This shows how many times members of staff need to contact each other or external agencies in the process of providing care for a patient. The hand off chart shown below is that of a single patient from leaving theatre following an orthopaedic operation to being discharged. This showed 197 hand offs between different members of staff.

This is a bewildering amount of complexity with a huge potential for delays, error and frustration. A patient who was on that team during the week remarked 'how did I ever escape from your hospital?'.

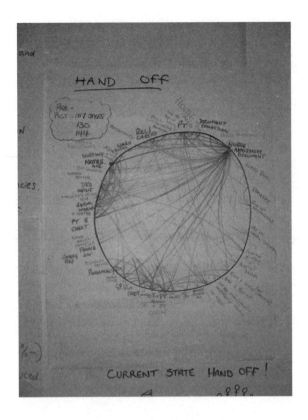

Fishbone diagrams

These are sometimes called cause and effect charts. They are useful to begin to probe more deeply in to the current state and understand the root causes of problems.

5 Whys

This is a technique for revealing the root cause of problems that are identified as part of the current state map. Our Pathology Manager recently reported at an outbrief, a 5 Why session which identified a relatively straight-forward solution to what had appeared to be an extremely difficult problem:

> Staff in the Blood Sciences Laboratory were being left at the end of the shift with a large number of samples that had not been processed. They believed that this was because there weren't enough staff to meet the processing demand. Their initial belief was that more staff needed to be recruited. The 5 Why exercise led to a reframing of the problem in the following way:

- We don't have enough staff to do the task – **Why?** Because there is a backlog of samples left at the end of every shift. **Why?** Because we have to keep stopping processing samples to clean the robot which handles the bottles. **Why?** The robot keeps jamming. **Why?** The labels haven't been fixed on the sample bottles properly making the bottles sticky, which clogs up the robot mechanism. **Why?** Staff haven't been properly trained in how to fix the labels on.

From this analysis a problem that had appeared to be about inadequate staffing levels was discovered in reality to be about inadequate training. The future state included standard work procedures and training for all staff in affixing labels to the bottles!

Making problems visible every day

Learning to See shouldn't simply be restricted to a valuestream analysis event. Staff are encouraged to wear their lean goggles every day and to look for waste in their processes. **Visual management** is an approach which can greatly help in this. This includes identifying simple measures of process performance and making sure that they are clearly displayed.

Control boards in wards, clinics and departments can show staff whether or not their team is delivering the desired goals. Examples of suitable measures to be displayed on control boards might include infection rates, complaints, theatre throughput against plan, or time spent in the A&E department by patients. However visual management extends far beyond the use of control boards. The idea is to make it readily apparent to everyone that a problem exists which needs to be fixed.

6S, which will be described in more detail in the next chapter, is a method for organising the workplace in such a way that problems are more readily apparent. If the ward, clinic or department is so cluttered and untidy that you can't see where the problems are then you don't have much chance of fixing them! For example, in a well organised environment equipment is stored on shadow boards. Once the piece of equipment is removed it is quite clear that it is missing as the outline of it remains painted on to the shadow board. There is a much higher likelihood in this circumstance that the equipment will be returned swiftly.

Shadow board

Similarly many hospital departments have vital equipment hidden behind cupboard doors. It can be highly frustrating to staff in a hurry, to open the cupboard only to find the piece of equipment is missing. If the cupboard doors are removed and areas for equipment clearly marked it is clear to anyone passing whether or not things are where they should be.

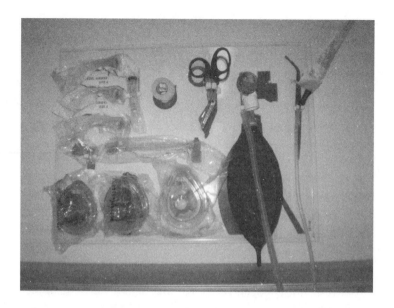

Case Study: Learning to see the patient's journey for people with fractured hips
During the lean redesign of the patient journey for those with fractured hips, the team conducted a great many mapping exercises! The first and the largest scale of these took place during the original valuestream analysis event. Here the whole process for a patient with a fractured hip was mapped backwards from the point of discharge. A variety of techniques were used to understand what was actually happening. These included spaghetti diagrams and hand off charts.

The mapping showed huge waste and the potential for error. There were often long delays for example in administration of pain relief, the correction of fluid balance and the administration of oxygen. Recognising the deterioration in the patients condition and acting on it was a significant risk. Finally getting senior clinical input and getting the patients quickly into theatre were problematic.

All of these delays had an adverse impact on the patient's experience and contributed to the high levels of excess mortality.

The spaghetti diagram showed that staff were walking miles when they didn't need to. This was because things weren't where they should have been when they were needed. This was not only equipment and information but sadly also patients. It was commented 'we had to go and look for sick patients and they might be anywhere across three or four wards'.

The hand-off chart was perhaps the most spectacular of all. This counted the number of interactions between different members of staff in order to achieve a result for the patients. The number of hand-offs just between the patients leaving theatre and being discharged was staggering. It contained an extraordinary 197 hand-offs. This represented a huge potential for frustration, error and delays.

As a patient on the team herself put it 'how did I ever get out of your hospital?'

Checklist for getting started on Learning to See

❑ Choose a topic that is of real importance to you

❑ Gather data and understand value from the patient's perspective

❑ Train staff in the Seven Wastes and examine your processes for evidence of these

❑ Organise a VSA event. If resources are limited or if the topic is a relatively small one you could run a mini VSA. Even a single day would be valuable. If you are able to be more ambitious then consider a full week long event

❑ Map the current processes and identify the non value added activity; spot opportunities for quick wins

❑ Find ways to make the waste and problems in your processes visible on a day to day basis and encourage staff to find ways to improve what they do.

References

1. Rother, M. & Shook, J. (1998) *Learning to See: Valustream mapping to add value and eliminate waste*, Brookline, MA: Lean Enterprise Institute.

Chapter Eight

Redesigning care*

SUMMARY

- The creative step in any lean transformation is the redesign of your service to tackle the problems you can see through 'lean goggles';

- Redesigning care is about effective care, being delivered through effective processes by effective teams;

- Improvement Plans to deliver a desired future state will consist of some large scale projects, some 'just do its' and some rapid improvement events;

- Rapid Improvement Events are as much about engagement as about improvement; they change attitudes and behaviours as well as achieving progress; they require thorough preparation, skilled facilitation and rigorous follow up;

- Improvement requires change; change is difficult and must be carefully managed with due respect to the people involved.

It is no use understanding what is of value to patients and learning to see problems within existing processes unless these insights are acted upon. Otherwise this activity in itself has been wasteful! Consequently the third phase of the BICS cycle – that of redesigning service delivery is critical. This involves developing an agreed vision of a challenging but achievable future state which can be realised within the next twelve months, together with a firm plan for making it a reality. This plan is likely to involve some major large scale projects, some 'just do its' and potentially also some rapid improvement events.

It is at this stage of the BICS cycle where imagination, ingenuity and courage are at a premium to envision and test out a new way of doing things.

This chapter describes the three essential building blocks of redesigning care as practiced within the Bolton Improving Care System. These are effective processes, effective practice and effective teams. It describes useful tools and approaches to delivering each

---

*I'm indebted to Flinders Hospital in Adelaide, South Australia for the term 'Redesigning Care'. Flinders use it to describe the whole of their lean approach; in Bolton it is the third phase of our BICS cycle.

of these. Rapid improvement events are a valuable vehicle for getting improvement to happen quickly on the ground and for altering attitudes and behaviours. Tips for running rapid improvement events successfully are offered. Finally, all improvement requires change but people don't always find change easy, especially if they are not the ones initiating it. Approaches to managing change effectively and ensuring that due respect for people is preserved are offered.

A three-pronged approach to redesigning care

It is in the redesign phase that the most active adaptation of a lean approach is required to make it suitable for the cultural context of healthcare organisations. For new ideas to take hold they need to appeal to the interests and needs of staff working within the organisation. They need to be explained in language that is, understandable and engaging. In this way a cultural foothold is established which allows the lean practitioner to gain a grip on the interest and motivation of the staff involved.

Lean concepts and methods are best introduced gradually and need to be blended in to the existing healthcare frame of reference. In Bolton this creative adaptation has taken the form of the redesigning care triangle:

Figure 18: Redesign triangle

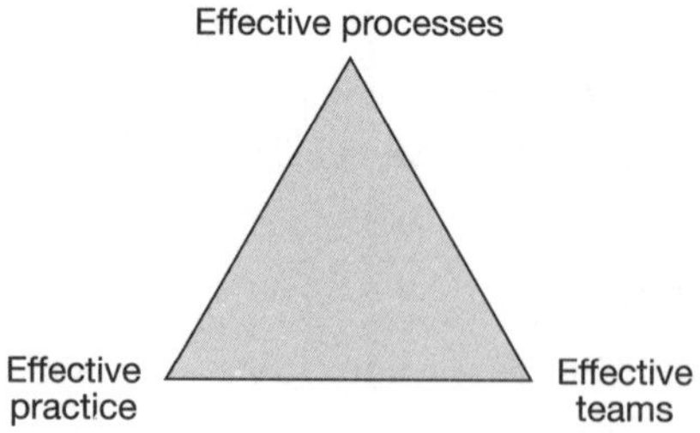

Effective processes

Effective practice

Effective teams

Most lean transformations are concerned primarily with effective processes. This involves the identification of value and non value adding steps, the elimination of waste, the removal of batching, the establishment of flow and the other process improvements which have helped to transform manufacturing operations. As was described in Chapters Three and Four, this approach to process improvement can be made readily applicable to healthcare and there is significant benefit to be derived from it.

A lean healthcare transformation will be even more powerful if the improvement to processes is given added leverage. This can be done by combining it with two other elements – the first is effective practice. In some ways this is similar to the lean concepts of standardised work and stable processes. In manufacturing, the development of standard work is achieved through experimentation, trial and error. In healthcare there is a worldwide research community dedicated to the identification of best evidence based clinical practice. Institutions such as the Cochrane Collaboration and the National Institute of Health and Clinical Excellence in the UK, conduct Meta analyses of research trials to draw conclusions about the most effective forms of practice. Any lean health-care organisation therefore that wishes to develop a standardised approach to work would do well to base that standard work on the best science available.

The final point of the redesigning care triangle is that of effective teams. Team working is a common feature of successful lean organisations in whatever sector they are found. Within healthcare the concept of the multidisciplinary team is a well established and important feature of the delivery of high quality care. Giving it emphasis within a lean healthcare redesign process has a cultural resonance in a healthcare setting whilst at the same time being a key ingredient in lean practice. Let's take each of these three elements in turn and explore them in more depth.

Effective processes

It is in the area of effective processes that perspectives from the world of lean can add most value. In Bolton we have used Simpler's helpful aide memoir which was first described in Chapter Four to prompt staff in the redesigning care phase of the BICS cycle.

Figure 19: Lean tools/principles

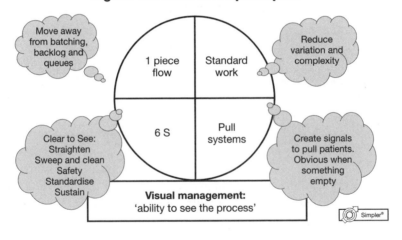

Let's look at a particular case example, that of the processing of blood samples in our laboratories. Like most laboratories, Bolton's was organised in professional silos. The different disciplines of haematology, chemistry, immunology and microbiology operated quite independently of each other. Each of them had a part to play in carrying out tests on patients blood samples so that the resulting information could be provided back to frontline clinicians to aid in diagnosis. Historically, each laboratory discipline had required its own blood sample and request form. Although some disciplines used the same types of machines to test the blood samples, these were housed in different laboratories and indeed even in different buildings! Furthermore samples waited in large batches for processing resulting in queues and delays of many hours and sometimes even days to deliver test results.

As a result of this the laboratory buildings were overflowing! A business case was in preparation for a multi-million pound development for an extension and concerns were regularly expressed by clinicians about the length of time which it took to produce test results.

The laboratory team was one of the first in the hospital to embrace the lean approach. It may be that there is something about the scientist's mind which is attracted towards the scientific approach to management implied in a plan-do-check-adjust cycle!

The story of the development of the lean blood sciences laboratory is described in more detail in Chapter Ten. The laboratory staff used a series of rapid improvement events to apply lean principles to the organisation of their work. The laboratories were reorganised using one piece flow to move samples to the appropriate test machine as soon as possible after arrival in the department. The analysers were relocated and laid out to improve flow and samples were tested by competent scientists from any discipline, rather than there being strict professional demarcations as had previously been the case. Effort was put in to reduce batch sizes and to improve processes on a continuing basis using standard work and lean problem solving tools. Finally, visual management was introduced to show whether or not the processes were in control and delivering the results expected.

This was far from an easy process and there were many difficulties and set backs. The results, however, were impressive. From the patients point of view there was a marked reduction in the number of blood samples that needed to be taken which also converted in to a saving for the hospital. Clinical staff on the wards experienced a reduction in the time taken in filling in request forms because now only one form was required. It was estimated that this saved over 50% of staff's time compared to the previous process. There was a significant improvement in turnaround times for a range of lab tests for example, thyroid tests being three times faster, haematinics four times faster and tests for C reactive protein ten times faster. Staff themselves in the laboratories walked an estimated 80% less distance than previously and the environment was calmer and less stressful. Finally the laboratory space required was reduced by over 50% and the potential costs of a major extension to the laboratories were avoided.

6S

One of the key elements within this redesign process was the use of 6S (most lean practitioners talk of '5S'. We have added a sixth – that of Safety. In healthcare environments it is particularly important that risk assessment and good health and safety practices are built into workplace design). This has been referred to on a number of occasions and it is often an important aspect of lean activity within healthcare. Interestingly, although people often think of healthcare environments as being clinical and well organised, this may sadly be far from the case. Some tips on conducting a 6S exercise are given in the diagram opposite.

Figure 20: BICS 6S Event

BICS
Bolton Improving Care System

Bolton Hospitals *NHS*
NHS Trust

Basic 6S Event – Standard Work

Step 1 Ensure appropriate materials are available
- Having the correct equipment is a must – steam cleaners, cleaning fluid, paint, rollers, floor tape, rags, label making machines, foam for drawers etc

Step 2 Establish standards
- Create a one-page standard to define standards for workplace organisation e.g. grey aisles, red work areas, blue material footprints, yellow lines, orange guards, standard benches and cabinets etc

Step 3 Identify the area for improvement
- Select an area based on the following criteria; 6S audit score, safety issues, small wastes evident from cell reviews, downtime – don't forget offices
- Take 'before' pictures and ensure a 'before' audit is available
- Set an improvement target for the team based on the audit score

Step 4 Assemble the appropriate team
- Mix of cell operators, staff and management. (Great early event format to break down barriers.)

Step 5 Train the team
- Explain the 6Ss and the event format. Visit another successfully 6S'd area if possible to create benchmark for the improvements required

Step 6 *Sort* out the contents of the area
- Attack the area and rapidly discard as much of the clutter and obsolete material as possible. Be aggressive – skip-loads of 'stuff' should be removed
- If serious doubt exists, red tag the item and place it in a holding area for review

Step 7 *Straighten* out the contents of the area
- Fix any safety-related problems and make decisions on the borderline items
- everything and everything in its place – create order and organisation
- Label items and their locations. Create footprints or shadow boards
- ors and fronts from cupboards to expose items and avoid clutter
- Create nests in drawers for tooling and gauges – arrange parts in order

ub
- Break out the 'elbow grease' – do some serious cleaning and examine equipment for wear and x obvious problems. Use maintenance team where required
- Completely paint the area per the standards; floor, walls, machines, racks etc

Step 9 *Safety*
- nsider risks and safety hazards in the area – implement low cost/no cost solutions.
- ndling where possible. Remove slip/trip opportunities.

andardise
- l weak spot of our 6S events – ensure this gets full focus. Create a simple work plan to rea in 6S order. Ensure you can tell quickly from looking at a visual aid that the tasks are pleted – this 'sustains the gain'.
- pictures to use for reference and compare to 'before' pics
- e cell to determine if the team have achieved their target

stain
- st of a good 6S event – sustain the improvements by regularly conducting a 6S audit mpler form. Post results on cell review boards. Use cell review visits to check the the area and drive ongoing improvement.

Simpler® | Reference material: Simpler Bu

6S can be used as a stand alone approach. Indeed some lean experts would argue that until a whole organisation is disciplined enough to maintain 6S consistently then it is not ready for more advanced lean concepts. I wouldn't go along with this but I would certainly agree that 6S is extremely valuable in a healthcare environment. It makes visible much of the hidden waste and problems which get obscured by the normal clutter of a busy ward, clinic or department. It importantly also helps prepare a work area for the establishment of flow as opposed to batched processes. It is essential to bear in mind however that 6S is not easy to implement and isn't simply a 'quick clean up'. Done properly it is time-consuming, requires training and initially at least some facilitation. The key to 6S is its sustainment over time.

So developing effective processes is the first part of our three pronged approach to redesigning care. Great value can be gained from it: it takes out waste and unnecessary steps, increases quality and reliability, decreases error rates, increases the amount of staff time available for value adding activity and raises staff morale. But, hospitals are not factories; the job of healthcare workers isn't the same as that of the assembly of motor parts. So along with effective processes, effective practice is key to the successful delivery of healthcare. This is true whether you are seeking to transform a clinical department or a back office function within a healthcare setting.

Effective practice

Effective practice can refer both to the technical delivery of work to a high standard, or to the human dimensions which surround that activity. For example effective practice incorporates both the correct aseptic technique when inserting a cannula into a patient's hand and also the care and compassion which empathises with the pain and discomfort this may cause the patient to feel.

Effective practice is incorporated in to redesigned care through BICS in two ways. Firstly by ensuring that redesigned services are based on the best evidence available; secondly by ensuring compliance with effective practice through the use of standard work or what is often referred to in healthcare terms as 'care bundles'. There is no shortage of evidence within healthcare about best available practice. Sadly all too often many of the known effective interventions are either not carried out at all or only given partial effect.

A good example of the inclusion of effective practice in to a redesigned service using lean methodology is that of stroke services in Bolton. Historically stroke services in UK hospitals have not been well designed. There is now a strong body of evidence about the essential features of a high quality stroke service. This includes material from the National Institute for Innovation and Improvement, national strategy on stroke services published by the Department of Health and the sentinel audit of stroke care conducted each year by the Royal College of Physicians.

Stroke patients should be carefully managed during the hyper-acute phase of their stroke i.e. during the first 72 hours. They should all receive a CT scan within 24 hours. Those patients who may benefit from thrombolysis (potentially up to 40% of stroke patients) should receive that CT scan within 3 hours of the onset of the stroke and have thrombolytic therapy initiated. In a very small number of cases surgical intervention may be appropriate. All stroke patients, whether they have received thrombolytic therapy or not, should initially be placed in an acute stroke ward where a thorough assessment can be conducted by a multidisciplinary team including a stroke consultant, physiotherapists as well as stroke specialist nurses. Ideally the length of stay of stroke patients will be kept to a minimum through the presence of an early supported discharge team which allows the continuation of rehabilitation within a community setting. For some stroke patients further inpatient rehabilitation may be necessary.

A valuestream mapping exercise was conducted on the whole of the stroke pathway which revealed many deficiencies compared to best practice. Bolton was not untypical of many UK hospitals in that it had poor initial access to a CT scan. Although it had an effective rehabilitation ward the patients were scattered through the hospital during the acute phase of their stroke and there was no dedicated acute stroke facility. Thrombolysis was not available. The team moved on to develop a future state vision for the stroke service and a plan for implementing it. That improvement plan has included the establishment of an acute stroke ward, availability of 24 hour CT scanning, access to a nearby tertiary centre for thrombolysis for those patients who can benefit from it, the development in conjunction with the primary care trust of an early supported discharge team and the relocation and further development of inpatient rehabilitation services. The existence of a template of effective practice upon which the lean redesign of the service could be based was an important ingredient in its successful transformation. At the same time the use of lean concepts such as 6S, flow, pull, visual management and standard work have greatly enhanced the implementation of known best practice.

Even where there is good quality evidence available and a strong clinical consensus about the best form of treatment, it is not always the case that there is good compliance with this. Within Toyota the standard work for critical operations is carefully mapped out and operators are trained to ensure they can fulfil the requisite steps in the right order and to the right level of quality. It is the job of supervisors to ensure that this is done and to provide coaching and support if employees demonstrate that they cannot satisfactorily follow standard work.

Within healthcare, the culture of the individual autonomy of professionals has often meant that failures to adopt the best available techniques have gone unchallenged. Techniques for applying standard work in healthcare do exist however. These are sometimes known as 'care bundles'. A care bundle is a series of interventions which if implemented consistently will dramatically improve the chances of a successful outcome for the patient. Research has shown that in many cases only four, three or even two out of five interventions within a care bundle are completed which significantly reduces the potential benefit for the patient.

It is in the area of effective practice that the various disciplines of clinical governance such as clinical effectiveness, research and development and clinical audit come together with the lean approach. Great benefit is to be gained by ensuring that staff working in these disciplines learn about lean methodologies and that those who are leading lean healthcare redesign are closely in touch with developments in evidence based practice.

As well as the correct delivery of clinical care, effective practice also incorporates the human dimensions of care delivery. A good example in Bolton Hospital is that of ward based cleaners – a group of staff whose role in caring for patients is often under-estimated. Patients are often likely to see far more of the cleaner on the ward than of their own consultant! A friendly and hospitable approach from a cleaner can help a patient's morale. It also inspires greater confidence in the attention being paid to cleanliness on the ward. Standard work for cleaning staff is now to speak with every patient on every ward each day to enquire how they are feeling and to check their satisfaction with the overall cleanliness and tidiness of the ward.

These two aspects, the technical delivery of services and the human dimensions apply just as much in back office settings as they do on the ward. For example, following best practice procedures in the accounting department or the HR function, will reduce error rates and improve the reputation and credibility of those departments.

High standards of customer service including courtesy and responsiveness are just as important in service departments as they are in frontline care delivery.

Effective teams

The third element in redesigning care is to ensure that it is delivered through effective teams. There is a great deal of evidence within healthcare of the importance of effective team working. A UK based charitable trust, the Health Foundation, has recently published a review from four pilot sites which are working to promote patient safety initiatives which has demonstrated the links between effective team working and a safer service. (1). The Royal College of Surgeons in a recent publication have reinforced this message and issued guidance on the best ways of building effective teams within a healthcare setting (2).

Developing effective team working is one of the core skills of a good manager or leader, a theme to which we will return in Chapter Ten. Within Bolton Hospital a number of mechanisms have been used to promote effective team working, these include allowing members of the team to get a better understanding of their individual preferred styles of working using tools such as 360° feedback and Belbin's team roles questionnaire. Skilled facilitation from our organisational development advisors has helped teams to become more effective and also to improve the working environment and quality of working life of individuals within them.

Not only are effective teams a key element of the lean redesign process in healthcare, lean activities themselves can be superb team building exercises. In particular we have found that valuestream analysis events and rapid improvement events have greatly strengthened team working in those areas where relationships were already sound and helped to surface and tackle potential problems in areas where team working was not well established. The value of using lean redesign to improve the work of teams in healthcare lies in its following qualities:

- It promotes a deep understanding at a practical level of the roles of the different members of the team which enhances communication and mutual respect
- It creates a recognition of the interdependence of the different members of the team
- It breaks down hierarchies and professional barriers which may get in the way of effective team working
- It creates a focus on the customer/patient as a unifying goal for all of the team members.

A good example of team development can be found in the redesign of the stroke patient journey referred to earlier. In this case the members of the multidisciplinary stroke team had felt that they had reasonable working relationships. However, once they began their detailed mapping of the service it became clear that there were a wide range of different perspectives and approaches. For example, the way in which patients and carers were involved in care planning varied greatly between different professional groups and there was duplication and overlap in assessment processes and in the way information was recorded. It was recognised that although team meetings and communication had taken place this was somewhat perfunctory and had failed to explore the really important issues. The participation of the team members in a redesign of the stroke patient's journey including the development of detailed standard work for the different members of the team greatly strengthened working relationships.

The vision of providing best possible care for stroke patients by using the Bolton Improving Care System proved to be a highly motivating unifying goal for the team members.

The improvement plan

So – the three elements in the redesigning care approach are to deliver effective practice through effective processes by effective teams. I described in Chapter Seven the mapping of a current state and the development of a vision of an improved future state. That future state will embody the redesign 'triangle'. It will be given effect through an Improvement Plan signed off by all the team members and by senior management in the Hospital. The plan is likely to consist of some large scale projects, some 'just do its' and some rapid improvement events.

Projects require careful planning and implementation. An example which was given earlier in the book consisted of the relocation of plain film x-ray equipment in to the orthopaedics department. This is both costly and logistically difficult and requires the support of senior managers within the Trust. It therefore needs a cost benefit evaluation and effective project management. At the other end of the spectrum are 'just do its'. These might include simple changes to paperwork or the removal of unnecessary steps which everyone agrees are obvious easy wins. In between these two are a range of improvements which require concerted effort and the agreement of a range of professionals but which don't need to be elevated to the highest levels of decision making within the organisation. All too often these kind of changes have languished in a no man's land. At best they have cycled through endless rounds of committees and consultation documents in the hope that someone will make a decision. As one hospital consultant pointed out to me 'It has felt in the past as though our systems have been purposely designed to prevent any action taking place!'. These are the types of issues which are ideally suited to being resolved through a rapid improvement event.

Rapid improvement events

Rapid Improvement Events are counter-cultural for most healthcare organisations. The whole idea that improvement can be rapid is something which staff initially find a little unsettling! Many healthcare organisations have found a way of accommodating the power struggles between different professional groups – doctors, nurses, therapists, managers, administrative staff, in a way which encourages conciliation and consensus. There is undoubtedly sense in this, but such processes have often been time consuming to deliver and have meant that many good ideas have fallen by the wayside. Rapid Improvement Events are different – they aim to make change happen within the space of a single week. The makeup of a rapid improvement event, is similar to a valuestream analysis event, (described in Chapter Seven) although teams are slightly smaller and a higher proportion of staff are drawn from the area on which the improvement is centred.

In Bolton we organise RIEs on a seven week cycle with three weeks' preparation, one week for the event and three weeks of follow up. For each RIE we identify a team leader, a facilitator from our Bolton Improving Care services team and an Executive Sponsor. Topics for rapid improvement events are many and various. A topic can be a one-off problem in a particular area or part of a much bigger overall improvement plan in an effort to improve an entire patient journey. Hotel DieuGrace, a Canadian Hospital, has found it useful to issue explicit ground rules for rapid improvement events. These are:

1. Respect each other at all times
2. No-one will lose their job as a result of this rapid improvement event
3. There are no more resources or staffing available
4. There is no more space.

The reassurance about impact on jobs is critical. Unless staff feel secure and confident that their jobs aren't under threat they are unlikely to be innovative and creative. It is also important to make it clear to staff that unlike working parties or committees, a rapid improvement event is not intended to be a vehicle for a bid for resources. The aim is to make the existing service work better. Often this can be done with fewer resources than the current poor quality service with all its inherent waste.

A five-day rapid improvement event

The pattern for a five-day rapid improvement event should be as follows:

Day one – training in lean concepts and simple tools for those who have not experienced them before; clear definition of the problem and agreement on success criteria.

Day two – analysis of the underlying causes of the problem. Tools which were introduced in Chapter Seven such as 5 whys and cause and effect diagrams are extremely useful here. Towards the end of day two, the team are encouraged to begin to use their creativity to come up with potential solutions to the problem.

Day three – some of the solutions begin to be tested out. This is sometimes called 'trystorming'. Another useful technique is to evaluate each option using scoring criteria, known as a 'beauty parade'. Towards the end of day three there should be sufficient data to choose between the different options for solving the problem.

Day four – consolidation in to practice and development of standard work. The proposed solution must be sustained after the end of the event. Therefore identifying how to do this during the RIE week itself is an important step.

Day five – summarising achievements and lessons: through presentation at a celebratory outbrief. As with the VSA, the Friday lunchtime outbrief is an important event. It is a way both of celebrating the hard work of the team, and also of publicising what they have done and seeking the support of their colleagues and other stakeholders for its continuation.

Rapid improvement events are a way of making changes happen quickly. They are almost even more important as an organisational development or cultural change intervention. They can have a dramatic effect on sceptical staff converting them in a short space of time in to lean enthusiasts. They help to reinforce and deepen lean skills and attitudes amongst those who are going through rapid improvement events for a second, third, fourth or even fifth time.

One of the difficulties with this effect is that the staff who take part can become evangelical about the changes which they have designed and implemented. This may lead to a bi-polar effect with those staff who haven't been involved reacting against this and becoming more sceptical and hostile than they were before the event. This highlights a critical issue regarding not only about rapid improvement events but redesigning care as a whole. Achieving improvement implies change, and this is always difficult for those directly affected. Change affects not just those staff who have been on the RIE, but also those working in the area are directly affected and potentially also staff in upstream and downstream processes.

Managing change

To avoid the potentially negative effects of change, organisations need to have standard work for managing the change process itself. The first step in this should be a stakeholder analysis to identify those groups who have an interest in the issue. In the example given earlier of the radiology plain film reporting cell, this included a variety of staff such as the radiologists themselves, the clerical staff who were typing and issuing reports, other staff in the department who were affected by the physical changes and altered work routines, as well as 'customers' in the referring departments and other staff who were tangential to the process such as those in transport and information. Having identified the stakeholders a force field analysis diagram can be drawn as shown below to identify what might inhibit change and what might support it:

Figure 21: Force field diagrams for radiology plain film reporting 'cell'

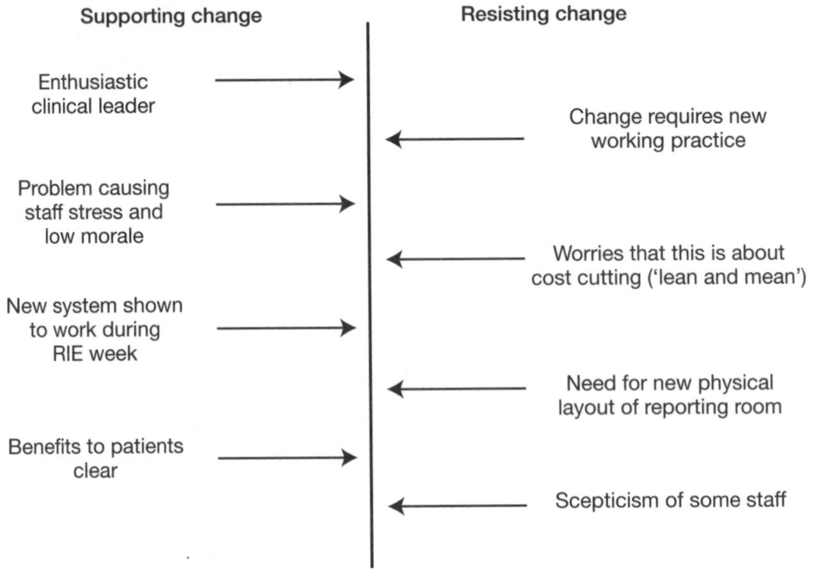

A further part of the standard work for managing change is to have an agreed approach towards understanding how people come to terms with the process of transition. A helpful model is that developed by William Bridges in his book 'Managing Transition' (3). Bridges turns on its head the normal thinking about the change process. This tends to be linear and to progress from a defined beginning through the middle of the process to the end. Bridges' view is that we need to start with the end! Any change implies the end of the current arrangements. This might include an office in which an individual feels at home, a team with which they feel comfortable, or a set routine with which they are familiar. Time and support needs to be given to allow people to come to terms with the loss of what they have been used to in the past. The middle of the change process is a 'neutral zone' where staff can begin to reach an accommodation with the new way of doing things. This paves the way for a new beginning in which the new conditions can become part of the normal way of working.

Managing transitions

Figure 22: Managing transitions

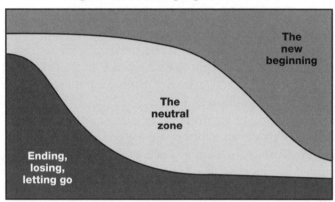

If the redesign of care is to be successful then healthcare organisations need to train staff, not just in quality improvement tools but also in the handling of people and in managing the human dimensions of change. Where staff in organisations are unionised, then it is particularly important to develop an effective working partnership with trade unions and professional associations when handling this phase of the lean redesign process. This issue is explored in more depth in Chapter Eleven. For now it is worth emphasising the need to invest time and effort in building relationships with staff side representatives that are based on integrity and mutual respect. The benefits of a lean transformation will ultimately be felt by staff as well as by patients, but the process of delivering change is rarely smooth or easy.

An ethos of cooperation and partnership working greatly helps in resolving the difficulties that will inevitably arise.

Case study: Redesigning care for patients with fractured hips
Armed with an understanding of what was really valuable to patients and with an in-depth knowledge of the current state of their processes, the team set out to develop a vision for their future state which was achievable within the next twelve months. They then developed an improvement plan to make this happen.

The plan was bold and ambitious! It demanded a whole range of 'just do its'. It also set out a plan to run six separate week long rapid improvement events in the A&E department; in Radiology; to create a post-operative trauma stabilisation unit;

to improve multidisciplinary team working; in theatres; and to create effective patient flow.

These week-long events were opportunities to involve different members of the 'team'. The team was now a virtual team encompassing professionals from different disciplines who worked in many departments and functions spread across the Trust. In the past they would never have seen themselves as a team or a system and probably each would have been unaware of the part that others played in the patient's journey.

The process of redesigning care was itself an effective team building exercise, drawing together these previously disparate individuals. The improvement plan included the redesign of processes to create standard work and establish a system that flowed smoothly. It also sought to base practice on the best evidence available. This included the need for more extensive medical input for this group of patients prior to their admission to theatre.

One of the most critical elements of the plan was the creation of the Trauma Stabilisation Unit. This was an eight-bedded bay on one of the Trauma wards. It was planned and implemented during a single week! Beds were rearranged, patients moved, consultants work plans altered and a toilet converted in to a storeroom. The staff involved had never believed that so much effective action could be taken so quickly in a hospital setting!

The six rapid improvement events that were run across this pathway all made their contribution to improving outcomes for patients. They also gave the staff who took part a new perspective on the way the service was delivered. They developed skills and capabilities in using lean methodology and gave everyone a sense that rather than being victims of a system that they couldn't control, they were in the driving seat and able to effect change for the better.

Checklist for getting started on redesigning care

❏ Make sure any proposals for change are directed towards a clear statement of value from the customer's point of view

❏ Be aware of the need to redesign practice as well as processes and to build effective teams

❏ Develop skills and knowledge in all three of these areas

❏ If utilising a rapid improvement event methodology recognise that this requires thorough preparation, skilled facilitation during the event week and rigorous follow up

❏ Never forget that change is not straightforward. Recognise the difficulties involved in changing the existing way of doing things and train leaders to manage change well

❏ Involve staff side representatives fully in this work, being open with them about the benefits and potential problems and working in partnership with them to resolve these.

References

1. Health Foundation (2007) *Better Team Working for a Safer Hospital*, Health Foundation Briefing, June.
2. Giddings, A. & Williamson, C. (2007) *The Leadership and Management of Surgical Teams*, London: Royal College of Surgeons of England.
3. Bridges, W. (2003) *Managing Transitions*, Cambridge MA: Parsens Books.

Chapter Nine

Delivering benefit

SUMMARY

- It's easy for enthusiasm to dissipate and for improvement activity to 'over-promise and under-deliver';

- The first step towards realising benefits is to develop clear goals and meaningful measures;

- 'Who's in charge?' is a critical question: clarity about roles and line management ownership of improvements are critical to sustainment;

- 'Following up like crazy' is an essential habit to develop; visual management makes this easier;

- Creating the right environment for sustainability is a responsibility of senior managers and is vital if the gains from lean improvement are to be held.

One of the truisms of quality improvement activity is that translating energy and enthusiasm into bottom line results is very difficult. This is true not just for lean but for all quality improvement efforts and not just in healthcare but in all sectors. Delivering significant improvement is not easy; holding the gains is even more of a challenge. Many column inches have been written by commentators and academics on the problem of sustainability.

Why is it so difficult to deliver sustainable benefits?

As we have already seen, rapid improvement events can create a tremendous 'buzz'. They are capable of converting sceptics in to enthusiasts for lean improvement. Staff questionnaires often show a sharp increase in staff motivation and morale amongst those who have been on event teams, but after the highs can come the lows! A sceptic who has become a champion only to have their hopes dashed is hard to bring back in to the fold. If improvement events gather a reputation for generating a lot of talk but little action, then they will quickly become discredited in the organisation.

So why might it be that quality improvement work fails to deliver the bottom line results that seem to be there for the taking? There are a number of possible reasons for this as shown below:

Factors which make sustainability difficult

- **Lack of clarity or agreement about aims**: all too often the participants in improvement activity have different perspectives on what they are hoping to get out of it. Managers may have target driven bottom lines in mind whilst clinical staff issues are more concerned with removing hassles from day to day work and providing improvements in the quality of care.

  Most commercial organisations who embark on lean use the dimensions of quality, cost, delivery and morale to establish their goals. These don't necessarily translate directly in to healthcare but can be creatively adapted. As mentioned previously, Bolton Hospital uses the four quadrants of improved health, best possible care, joy and pride in work and value for taxpayers money to establish agreed aims.

- **Lack of credible measures**: at times healthcare organisations can appear to be data free zones! Given that medicine is a science and much of clinical practice depends on the derivation of patient specific data on which decisions are based, it's perhaps surprising that management decision making in healthcare is all too often based on speculation and organisational politics. One of the difficulties is that data is often collected for purposes other than improvement. The information that is needed to deliver accountability to government or to insurers may not be relevant or useful for quality improvement purposes.

- **Improvement initiatives can be seen as disconnected one off projects**: all too often healthcare staff don't see the resolution of problems and the improvement of quality as a part of their day job. Initiatives such as six sigma or lean are disconnected from daily activity and become the province of a limited few enthusiasts.

- **Organisational politics or inertia opposes change**: healthcare organisations are made up of a complicated mix of sub-cultures and power structures. Resistance to change can come from many different sources ranging from powerful medics to recalcitrant administrators who have lots of opportunity to block progress.

- **Lack of leadership skills and knowledge**: all improvement requires change and this must be handled sensitively and effectively if it is to produce beneficial results.

When reviewing this list you might wonder how anybody has ever the courage to embark on an improvement effort! But many have succeeded in overcoming these difficulties. The first step is to recognise their existence and then to develop strategies for dealing with them. Fortunately the potential gains in terms of improved services to patients, better value for money and enhanced staff morale are so enticing that they provide all the motivation that is needed to wrestle these problems to the ground.

Sustaining improvement is a challenge at the level of a ward, clinic or department and even more so when the aim is to transform a whole patient journey. Unfortunately there is yet another layer of problems and challenges for those seeking transformation across a whole hospital or an entire healthcare system. Chief Executives and Boards who engage in this kind of activity need to be mindful of the difficulties they will face and have the firmness of purpose and tenacity to stay the course.

Challenges facing senior managers and boards

- **Balancing short term pressures against a longer term drive for improvement:** Transformation programmes rarely pay dividends overnight. Indeed some research suggests that in healthcare it takes 15-20 years to establish a sustainable improvement orientated culture across a whole hospital. In the meantime important stakeholders will continue to expect short term results to be delivered, whether these be financial or service-based targets. Boards need a strategy which can allow them to 'stay on the pitch' long enough to put in place the building blocks of a long term transformation.

- **Commitment of the whole board**: a lean transformation requires a fundamental change to the way in which the organisation is managed. Evidence from a wide range of sectors shows that this will only happen if the whole board is committed and understands what is required.

- **Constancy of leadership**: perhaps the single biggest reason for the non-sustainability of a lean transformation is that an enthusiastic Chief Executive who has championed it moves on from the organisation to be replaced by someone who is not inclined to maintain the thrust and direction of the programme. This is a particular challenge in healthcare – in the English National Health Service the life span of Chief Executives in any particular job is under two years, which does not make consistency of purpose easy to develop!

- **Intra-organisational politics within a healthcare system**: where there is the ambition to extend a lean transformation outside the boundaries of a hospital to include primary care services, local authorities, the independent sector and voluntary agencies, then the challenges already described are magnified many times. There is no quick fix for this – only the painstaking time consuming job of building trust and relationships and developing a shared language and approach that is focussed on the needs of those using services rather than those providing them.

So, what can be done to overcome these obstacles and ensure that your lean improvement effort delivers bottom line results for patients, staff and taxpayers? You need to do the following:

- Establish clear goals and measures
- Clarify roles and responsibilities
- Follow up like crazy
- Create a culture that supports improvement.

Goals and measures

Delivering benefit is the last phase of the improving care cycle but its success depends on what is done right at the outset of any improvement effort. Identifying the problem to be fixed, and the goals and measures to be used are essential pre-requisites of delivering benefit. The framework used in Bolton Hospital is as shown:

Figure 23: Framework for measuring progress

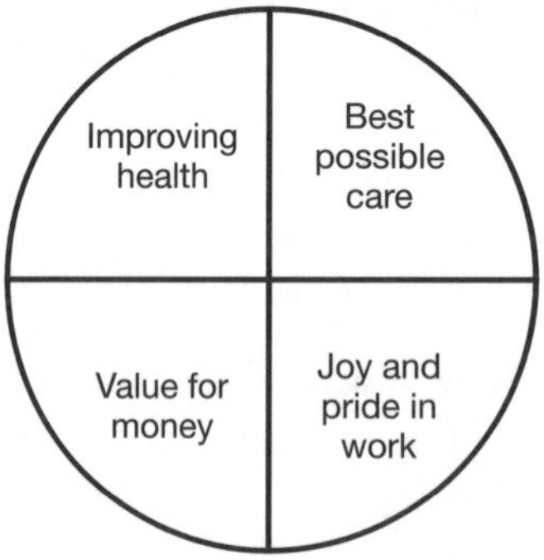

This framework is used to measure progress towards the Trust's overall business objectives as well as measuring improvements in particular patient journeys or for improvement activity at the level of the ward, clinic or department. All valuestream analysis events or rapid improvement events have an 'A3' document which makes these aims explicit.

Toyota use an A3 reporting format. In an A3, the definition of the problem, the analysis of the factors involved, the counter-measures to be attempted, the progress made and lessons learned are captured on a single A3 sheet of paper. Some organisations fall in to the trap of thinking that this is simply about reducing the amount of paper produced (though this in itself has some obvious benefits!) The real challenge of A3s is not producing a single sheet of paper but the thinking that is necessary to refine the issues and strip them down to their bare essentials. Once mastered it is not only a powerful technique for producing greater clarity of thinking, but also a useful communications vehicle.

Making aims explicit and ensuring a debate about them amongst all of the stakeholders involved isn't always easy but it is essential to resolving any underlying tensions or disagreements. We need to be open about the need to improve productivity and deliver value for money, but at the same time we need to accept that productivity improvement is unlikely to be a prime motivator for many clinical staff. Fortunately experience in applying lean to healthcare demonstrates that in the overwhelming majority of cases, efforts to improve the quality and safety of the patient's experience also produce a more efficient service.

Providing the right treatment and diagnosis quickly produces a speedier recovery, a shorter length of stay and reduces the need for further expensive tests or treatment. This approach holds true at the service level and also for whole organisations. A mission statement to be the 'cheapest provider of healthcare' is hardly likely to be motivating (and potentially worrying for patients!). On the other hand, the aim to be the 'best possible provider of care' is an aspiration which is both challenging and engaging. Of course lofty aspirations are pointless if they remain mere rhetoric. Ensuring bottom line delivery requires that those aspirations are turned in to tangible measures.

Don Berwick of IHI has pointed out 'all improvement requires change but not all change is an improvement'. To be sure that the changes we are making are actually for the better we need to measure before and after any quality improvement activity. Those measures need to be valid and reliable and the data on which they are based must be credible to avoid any claims of improvement being received with scepticism. This is particularly true in healthcare where high levels of proof using randomised control trial methodology are demanded for the introduction of new medical treatments and techniques.

Improvement activity is a 'pragmatic science' which may at first seem alien to those schooled in more traditional academic methods. Nevertheless the requirement to collect reliable data, to scrutinise it rigorously and to make an honest appraisal of the findings holds good. The NHS Modernisation Agency in the UK produced a booklet called Measurement For Improvement which is an excellent guide to using data for improvement purposes (1) It shows how to:

- Choose meaningful measures with clear definitions
- Establish a baseline
- Set a target for improvement
- Report in a way that allows effective judgements to be made.

The IHI 100K Lives Campaign had the memorable slogan 'soon is not a time, some is not a number' which captures wonderfully the importance of precise quantification.

Just as important as gathering data is analysing it in a meaningful way. I am sure we have all been in situations where a report is tabled in a meeting and those present simultaneously leap to the wrong conclusions. Comparing one month's worth of data in a table, to the previous month's data can be highly misleading. The fact that one number is bigger or smaller than another does not constitute a trend! It's impossible to assess whether progress is being made without a sense of the historic direction of travel as the charts overleaf illustrate.

Figure 24: Data analysis pitfalls

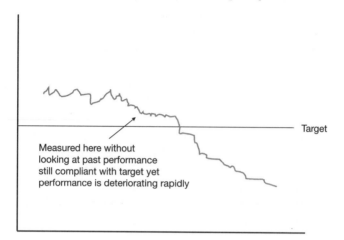

Measured here without looking at past performance still compliant with target yet performance is deteriorating rapidly

Target

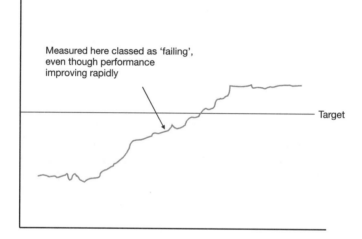

Measured here classed as 'failing', even though performance improving rapidly

Target

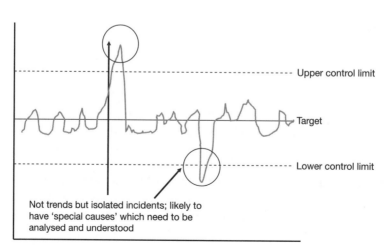

Upper control limit

Target

Lower control limit

Not trends but isolated incidents; likely to have 'special causes' which need to be analysed and understood

Run charts such as the ones shown opposite which plot performance over time are an excellent way of understanding underlying trends. A more sophisticated form of run charts are known as statistical process control charts. These plot the statistically derived upper and lower control limits and also identify the target which is being aimed for. Such SPC charts are used in everyday clinical practice for example, temperature charts or blood pressure graphs and so are often familiar to clinical staff.

Setting clear goals and using measurement honestly to tell what works from what doesn't is critical to delivering benefit from improvement activity. It avoids over-claiming for successes and allows you to understand when things aren't working as they should. There is often as much to be learned from instructive failures as there is from the easy wins!

Clarity of roles and responsibilities

A commonly heard comment in many organisations is 'we've got a quality improvement team, shouldn't they be fixing the problems … we're just too busy!' This is the mindset that can allow for the marginalisation of quality improvement activity. Toyota and other organisations where there is a genuine culture of continuous improvement would find this difficult to understand. In these organisations, it is everyone's job not only to carry out their allotted tasks but to find ways every single day of improving the way in which that job is done. In such organisations every employee is a problem solver and every working day is an opportunity for improvement.

A successful lean transformation in healthcare hinges on the degree to which line management, including clinical leaders, have ownership of the problems and accountability for delivering results. Where a ward manager, a medical consultant or a specialist nurse takes on the role of driving lean improvement, then it makes the leap from a project or an initiative into a change in the way we do things around here. Where those in critical leadership positions are sceptical or opposed, then no amount of enthusiastic facilitation from an external improvement team is likely to produce sustainable results. Within Bolton Hospital we have recognised that a triumvirate of roles are needed: that of the team lead, the executive sponsor and the BICS team facilitator.

The team leader

This should be someone with ownership of the process at an appropriate level in the line management structure. This gives them both control over resources and accountability for results. For example, in the case of the plain film reporting cell within radiology, the radiology department manager (who was also the senior radiography professional) took on the team lead role. Because she was held accountable for the backlog in plain films and had managerial control over the department, she was able to secure the necessary changes both in physical layout and in working practices. Sometimes a team approach to leadership is helpful. In the patient journey for stroke for example, co-team leaders have been appointed who are the lead consultant, specialist nurse and senior therapist in stroke services. These three are working together to drive changes across the whole of the stroke pathway. Where more than one individual is in a leadership role, then understanding the part each plays and their respective responsibilities is critical.

Whether an individual or team is given accountability it is important that they understand that it is their job to:

- ensure delivery of results
- link improvement activity to the mainstream of day to day working
- brief all staff of potential changes and secure their support
- unblock obstacles and confront those who are opposed to change in ways that will win them over.

Executive sponsor

Sometimes team leaders feel that they need more 'organisational clout' than they possess themselves (although in many cases the team leaders are experienced and highly respected clinical professionals which gives them influence and power far greater than they realise or than might be expected from their nominal position in the hierarchy). In order to give added emphasis to the importance and urgency of the improvement effort major BICS activities also have an executive sponsor.

Bolton Hospital has an Executive Board which consists of the Executive Directors of the hospital together with the Associate Medical Directors and General Managers of the operating Divisions (Anaesthetics & Surgery, Medicine & Emergency Care, Women's & Children's Services, Diagnostics & Therapies and Facilities). Taking the earlier two examples, the Executive Sponsor for the stroke work is the Associate Medical Director for Medicine & Emergency Care and for the radiology plain film reporting cell it is the Divisional Manager for Diagnostics & Therapies. The job of the Executive Sponsor is:

- to make links to other departments and functions
- to be an advocate for the changes that are needed at Trust Board level
- to provide constructive challenge to their team to keep them on track and ensure long term sustainability.

In the early days of our work the executive sponsors tended to underestimate how influential they can be. Visits from them to see teams in action and to look at results can be highly motivating. Knowing that your executive sponsor is going to turn up on a frequent basis and ask for progress reports focuses the mind on collecting measures and following through on agreed improvements. The team leads and executive sponsors are experts in their own processes but not necessarily in quality improvement methods and so need external expertise and facilitation. This is provided by the BICS team of facilitators.

BICS facilitators

The BICS team is small but perfectly formed! In the first two years of Bolton's lean transformation between 2005 and 2007, the team consisted of just five individuals and during 2007 has been doubled in size. This has been done through secondments of staff from the various parts of the hospital. The aim is to provide staff with twelve months in-depth experience of BICS work so that they can transfer that knowledge back in to their own departments.

None of the team had previous experience of lean but have received intensive training, guidance and support from our Simpler sensei. They have also visited other organisations which have undergone lean transformations and actively participated hands-on in improvement work in those other organisations. Their learning curve has been steep but their level of enthusiasm and motivation is extremely high. Their role is:

- to ensure the integrity of the BICS approach and the proper use of lean tools and methods
- to provide help, guidance, training and facilitation to teams engaged in improvement activity
- to be connectors and spreaders of good practice from one part of the organisation to another
- to lever in outside help from Simpler sensei or from other organisations
- to establish standard work for the reporting of results to allow for effective follow up.

Executive Board and the Chief Executive

The Executive Board and the Chief Executive maintain an overview of all major elements of BICS activity. They are responsible for ensuring the fit between BICS aims and the overall business objectives of the hospital. This involves monitoring the generic goals of the BICS work itself such as the numbers of staff involved in rapid improvement events as well the outcomes of specific improvement activity.

Improvement events are normally run on one week in the month and there maybe as many as four or five teams operating during that week. Each month, the Executive Board receives reports on the outcomes from events run in the previous month and signs off the aims for the events to be run in the coming month. This establishes a structure and discipline and helps set the pace of the improvement work.

Because many members of the Executive Board are Executive Sponsors for particular BICS projects, they have a vested interested in keeping themselves up to date and ensuring that their own pieces of work are progressing well. Peer pressure can be an important motivator in such situations!

In addition to this corporate review process, the Chief Executive also conducts reviews of the valuestreams that are being redesigned. This involves meeting with the Executive Sponsors, Team Leads and BICS facilitators to check progress against the initial goals, to consider what has been learned and to agree the next phase of the work.

Follow up like crazy

Robert Neiman in his book 'Execution Plain and Simple' suggests that one of the keys to successful delivery of results is the ability to 'follow up like crazy without driving people crazy' (2). It is essential to get this balance right

Figure 24: Stay on track

Laissez-
faire

Obsessive
control

No   No

Best path

Criteria
• Keep work moving productively
• Build capability and self-reliance of people
• Catch problems early and adjust
• Avoid getting yourself trapped in your own programme

The aim of follow up is to help unblock obstacles and demonstrate senior management commitment whilst at the same time leaving the responsibility and ownership with those on the ground. Too dictatorial an approach can feel like a bureaucratic burden and be demotivating for those on the front line. A lighter touch risks allowing inertia to develop with the consequence that results will be sub-optimal.

The style which leaders use in following up is of critical importance. The key to ensuring responsibility stays where it belongs is to adopt a questioning or coaching style.

There are a range of mechanisms which are useful as part of follow up. These include:

• Data reports
• Written reports
• Formal meetings where outbriefs on improvement activity are part of a regular agenda alongside financial and service performance
• One to one contact with team leaders
• Team progress review meetings
• Site visits

Site visits are particularly critical. The are sometimes known in lean terminology as 'Gemba walks' (Gemba is the Japanese term for the actual workplace). It is essential for leaders who are interested in the delivery of results to see progress and understand problems for themselves at first hand. This level of personal attention from a Director or Chief Executive makes a huge difference to the motivation of staff and to their understanding of how importantly their efforts are regarded within the organisation.

Creating a culture of sustainment

There is a risk that healthcare organisations can do all of this – developing effective goals and measures, clarifying roles and following up vigorously – only for it to be frustrated by an underlying culture of opposition or indifference. It would be a pity if the attention paid to delivering results was just a finger in the dyke and the opportunity was missed to build the dam properly in the first place!

The National Institute for Innovation and Improvement in the UK has produced a useful guide to sustaining quality improvements (3). This is grounded in research previously done by the NHS Modernisation Agency, its predecessor organisation.

The framework used by the Institute is set out below:

Figure 25: NHS institute framework for sustaining quality improvements

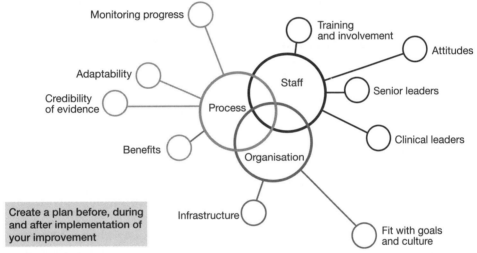

The Institute's model sets out the elements that need to be considered in building a culture that will sustain improvement. This cultural dimension reinforces the strong connections between quality improvement and organisational development which is one of the most important aspects of a lean approach.

Clarity about benefits, the credibility of the evidence to be collected, the likelihood that improvements can be adapted and sustained over time and the arrangements to monitor progress are all important features that need to be taken in to account. As far as staff are concerned, training and development in effective change management, tools and techniques is absolutely critical. The alignment of aims and values between senior leaders in the organisation, including clinical leaders, and an acceptance of the need to change are also critical issues. Finally sustainability is much more likely if the aims of the improvement effort have a close fit with the goals and culture of the organisation and if an infrastructure has been put in place to support and maintain the quality improvement.

One of the primary roles of any Chief Executive and Board which aspires to be lean must be to put in place these cultural building blocks to sustain improvement. The Boards of such organisations will be involved in regular debate and discussion about how best to measure benefits, about the education and development needs of staff, about the infrastructure that is needed to support their improvement activity and about how all of this fits with their overall organisational vision and goals. The leaders in such an organisation will be social architects designing and building a lean healthcare culture that will be significantly different to that traditionally experienced in healthcare. This challenge is explored in more depth in section three of this book.

Case study – delivering benefit for patients with fractured hips

The Trauma team were clear at the outset about the goals they were striving to deliver. Pre-eminent amongst these was improved mortality. At the end of the redesign period they were able to point to the following results:

- A 42% reduction in paperwork for the staff involved
- Faster recovery and lower demand on the rehabilitation ward
- Total length of stay reduced by 33%
- Mortality reduced by 38%
- The relative risk of death reduced to 105.5 from the previous 174.4

Twelve months after the BICS redesign the results had improved still further. By the end of 2007 the relative adjusted risk stood at 88 – a 50% improvement on the starting position. These were astonishingly impressive results in such a short space of time. This is even more true given the previous unsuccessful attempts over almost a decade to bring about improvement in this service.

The team are currently remapping the whole process again with the aim of pushing the improvement further and making the service leading edge in terms of quality and performance. They are also firmly committed to continuing to measure progress and are using data on a day by day, week by week basis to seek further improvements. To this end they have created an 'Information Centre' not only for fractured hips but for the whole of the orthopaedic service, which is displayed close to the orthopaedic wards.

At the Trust's Annual Achievement Awards in July 2007, the Trauma team picked up a host of team and individual awards. These were well deserved. The redesign of the patient journey for those with fractured hips had shown the potential of what lean could deliver – better care for the patients; greater satisfaction for staff and better value of taxpayer's money all at the same time.

> ## Checklist for getting started on delivering benefit
> ❏ Before embarking on any lean redesign within a department, a patient journey, a whole hospital or a healthcare system, get clear agreement on goals and aims
>
> ❏ Select measures carefully. They should be credible, valid and reliable – and present them in a way that creates intelligent information
>
> ❏ Ensure clarity of roles and line management ownership for improvement activity; it should not be seen as a separate project or add on
>
> ❏ Develop a management style that follows up vigorously without demoralising or taking back responsibility from front line staff
>
> ❏ Build a culture of sustainment by paying attention to processes, leadership and organisational culture.

References

1. NHS Modernisation Agency (2002) *Improvement Leader's Guide to Measurement for Results*.
2. Neiman, R. (2004) *Execution Plain and Simple*, New York: McGraw Hill.
3. NHS Institute of Innovation and Improvement (2004) *Complexity of Sustaining Healthcare Improvements: What have we learned so far?*, Research in Practice Report, No. 13, October.

Section Three

Embedding lean in to healthcare's DNA

Section One of this book gave an understanding of the concepts that underpin a lean approach and showed how these can be applied in a healthcare setting. Section Two provided a framework for lean transformation in healthcare and gave some practical tips on how to get started. This third and final section is for those who want to go further.

The determined lean healthcare pioneer won't be satisfied with just understanding the terminology and being able to talk confidently about the concepts. Even a series of successful Kaizen events will ultimately be less than satisfying. Genuine success will only be in sight when lean healthcare ceases to be a project or a catchphrase and becomes a daily activity.

In the truly lean healthcare organisation every member of staff will be a problem solver every single day of their working lives. Achieving this is by no means an overnight task. After two years of effort in Bolton Hospital with many 'instructive failures' we are seeing the first glimmerings of lean healthcare as a daily activity. Chapter Ten sets out one example of where this is beginning to happen, in Bolton Hospitals Blood Sciences Laboratory.

The Bolton Improving Care System provides a model for continuing cycles of lean improvement. BICS also embodies a series of underpinning activities which the hospital believes are necessary to sustain lean healthcare and embed it in the organisations' culture. These include developing the skills and capabilities of all members of staff, creating lean support functions, establishing a human resources framework to handle the people issues which lean transformation throws up and creating a leadership and management style that is appropriate in a lean environment. Chapter Eleven explores these issues in more depth and provides examples of the way in which they are being tackled in Bolton.

The concluding chapter of this book is more personal in nature. Chapter Twelve sets out my reflections on the challenges which I have faced in striving to adapt lean in to a healthcare setting. Although these are only my own experiences, I know from talking to others who are on the same journey that they seem to strike a chord. Hopefully they will be of help to any reader who is looking down this path and wondering whether to take that precarious first step themselves.

Chapter Ten

Making lean healthcare a daily reality

SUMMARY

- **Lean transformations often get stuck in an endless cycle of Kaizen events; a truly lean organisation changes daily behaviours;**

- **This involves fundamental changes to the work of teams and supervisors including:**
  - **the development of standard work for processes and for team leaders**
  - **the creation of a visual management system**
  - **the establishment of daily accountability processes**
  - **extensive training in the new approach**
  - **persistence and determination;**

- **Bolton's Blood Sciences Laboratory have taken their first tentative steps towards making lean healthcare a daily activity in this way.**

I have a bad habit. I enjoy reading (or rather as a former History graduate, speed reading i.e. skipping the boring bits!) and so I have read as much as I can about lean transformations. The bad habit involves my suggesting to everyone else in my organisation that they should read the same books! From time to time someone retaliates and I always enjoy it when they do. I was absolutely delighted therefore when a member of our Pathology team recommended to me that I should read Creating a Lean Culture by David Mann (1).

Mann's book has heavily influenced the content of this chapter and provides an excellent framework for those wanting to move their lean improvement effort out of the realm of Kaizen events and in to day to day practice in the wards, clinics and departments.

Interestingly Mann is not a typical lean practitioner. He didn't start life as an engineer or even a quality improvement specialist. By training he is an organisational psychologist. His interest in brownfield lean conversion projects lies in studying the kind of leadership and the type of management systems which are needed to achieve a lean transformation. He believes this to be the missing link in the literature that has so far been published on the lean approach. The challenge is to shift the way workers think and act on a daily basis from a mass production mindset to that of lean production:

Table 6: Creating a lean culture

Mass production: personally focused work practices	Lean production: process focused work practices
Independent	Interdependent, closely linked
Self-paced work and breaks	Process-paced work, time as a discipline
'Leave me alone'	'I work as part of a team'
'I get my own parts and supplies'	In- and out-cycle work are separated and standardized
'We do whatever it takes to get the job done; I know whom I can rely on at crunch time'	There's a defined process for pretty much everything; follow the process
'I define my own methods'	Methods are standardised
Results are the focus, do whatever it takes	Process focus is the path to consistent results
'Improvement is someone else's job; it's not my responsibility'	Improvement is the job of everyone
'Maintenance takes care of the equipment when it breaks; it's not my responsibility'	Taking care of the equipment to minimize unplanned downtime is routine
Managed by the pay or bonus system	Managed by performance to expectations

Source: D. Mann (2005)

The pathology team at Bolton Hospital weren't just academically interested in Mann's ideas, they were keen to try them out for real. Their ambition was to manage the laboratory in a totally different way to anything that had been attempted before. Before setting out the main elements of what they describe as their laboratory lean management system it is worth just giving a little background to the nature of this service.

The Bolton Pathology Department and Lean Blood Sciences Laboratory

The pathology department consists of 185 staff. Many of these are highly trained scientists who have worked for many years to sub-specialise within their particular discipline. The department is split in to two sets of laboratories and offices separated by the main hospital corridor. When I arrived at Bolton in September 2004, one of the first visits I made was to the pathology laboratory. This was because they were running a strong lobbying campaign for a multimillion pound investment to create an extension to the department. It was certainly clear that they were pushed for space. Piles of stocks, samples awaiting processing and scientific and administrative staff seemed to cram every room. The impression was one of clutter and frenzied activity. The hospital couldn't afford the capital investment needed but it was also clear that the current conditions were far from ideal.

This dilemma was one of the primary reasons why pathology was an early test bed for our lean healthcare work. Many of the challenges which we faced in taking out unnecessary steps and delays in patient journeys involved the laboratory. In busy periods, especially during the winter months, the hospital was struggling to process patients waiting assessment in the emergency department and the turnaround time for blood tests was critical to this. Furthermore, our senior scientists could see significant income generation possibilities for the hospital if outsourced laboratory work could be brought back in house.

Over a twelve month period the Pathology Department engaged staff in numerous training activities, process mapping exercises and rapid improvement events. They gradually evolved a plan to reshape the department. What had historically been six discreet functions were drawn together in to a single unit – the Lean Blood Sciences Laboratory. Walls were knocked through, equipment relocated and work processes fundamentally redesigned. This was by no means a straight-forward process! The Pathology management team were faced with almost daily set backs. Morale in the department went down rather than up and it was often hard to identify clear benefits but the team showed resilience and determination.

The team gradually picked off the problems one by one. They involved more and more staff in training activities and in improvement events. Slowly the benefits began to become clear. Eighteen months later the team had generated 10% extra income with 2% fewer staff. The amount of floor space had been reduced by 40% which enabled testing work done elsewhere to be brought back in house and new contracts to be secured. The turnaround times for blood tests in the emergency department were dramatically reduced. At the outset we hadn't even been sure what they were! What's more, once the target of a turnaround time of two hours was achieved the team themselves decided that it was time to make the target harder and raised the bar so that the new goal became a turnaround time of one hour, forty-five minutes (the team leader already has his sights set on a one hour, thirty minutes aim, once this new goal has been consistently achieved).

It was against this background of eighteen months worth of effort, determination, set backs, recriminations and hard won successes that the Pathology management team took up the challenge of embedding lean as a daily activity within their work.

The laboratory lean management system

The team drew heavily on David Mann's work in setting out a framework by which they would manage the blood sciences laboratory in a new, different and they hoped, lean manner. The key elements were these:

- Standard work
  - For workstations
  - For leaders

- Visual controls
  - Production control boards
  - Metrics
  - Workstations
- Daily accountability processes
  - Daily meetings of work groups
  - Daily meetings of supervisors
- Training
  - Awareness
  - Tools
- Discipline
  - Persistence and determination.

Over time the team have recognised that the elements of this system are heavily inter-dependent. What's more, it is a system that is constantly in need of refinement and rein-forcement. Let's look at each element in more depth.

Standard work

The Pathology management teams' definition of standard work is that it is the current best practice which forms the baseline for continuous improvement. The aim of standard work is that the same task should be conducted in the same way every time. This involves developing a standard takt time (i.e. the time which a task should take and hence the pace at which processes need to move throughout a shift); a standard in-process inventory (i.e. the number of samples to be processed and dealt with in a given time period); and a standard work sequence (i.e. the order in which processing steps should take place is also defined).

When the team first started their work they found that there was no current accepted best practice! Each work team within the laboratory and indeed each member of staff had their own way of doing things. Whilst these broadly generated the desired end result there was little consistency and it had never occurred to anyone to discuss what the best way of doing things might be.

Many of the case examples of lean healthcare are in laboratory settings. Perhaps there is something in the scientists' mindsets which readily grasps that the PDCA cycle is the same as developing a hypothesis, testing it out, gathering data and learning from the results. This is how the team progressed in developing and agreeing standard work for the most important tasks within the laboratory. Following Mann's lead, the team went beyond this. They began to think not just about the standard work for those processing blood specimens but for team leaders and the pathology managers themselves.

If the work of the scientists who were processing samples had been somewhat haphazard and uncoordinated it was positively rigorous and systematic when compared with the jobs of their leaders! These often seemed to involve fire-fighting or struggling to implement whatever the latest directive was to emerge via email. A great deal of time was spent in meetings which were long and arduous treks through multipoint agendas.

In developing standard work for leaders, it became clear that it was important for them to meet with the team at the beginning of every shift to review the problems from previous shifts and how they were going to be tackled. It was also important for them to liaise with other colleagues in management to consider problems that could only be resolved through cross-functional or cross-departmental efforts.

Systematising the leader's job in this way was a novelty, yet it proved vital to embedding lean healthcare as a daily activity. Standard worksheets have been developed to guide leaders on how to carry out daily problem solving with their team.

Visual controls

The second key element within the Pathology Department's lean management system for the Blood Sciences Laboratory was the establishment of visual management systems. Visual management is a way of making it plain whether or not a process is in control and whether everything is as it should be. The pathology department management shared with me a wonderful example of a shadow board which is shown in the photograph below:

Initially, I was somewhat concerned that such sharp and dangerous looking objects should be present in the Blood Sciences Laboratory. Fortunately the manager admitted to me that this was a photograph he had taken whilst on holiday in San Francisco. It's a 1930s example of a shadow board taken from the prison kitchens in Alcatraz Prison. In such a setting, with many convicted murderers and felons, it was essential to make sure that knives and machetes didn't go missing! The shadow board is a useful visual trigger as to whether vital equipment is all present and correct.

Visual management

The visual representation of data was also critical to communicating to the team how well their system was performing. Data in healthcare settings are often displayed via computer screens and on complicated charts and diagrams. The lean blood sciences team took the view that simple manually produced charts filled in every day were far more effective. Indeed the senior biomedical scientist for the department, our Associate Medical Director for Diagnostics & Therapies, keeps his own personal chart which he fills in in his office every morning! A picture of this is shown below:

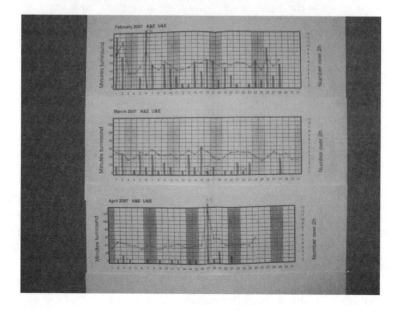

The fact that he pays such personal attention to visually tracking progress in this way isn't lost on the other members of his team and sends a powerful signal about the importance of real time data.

Daily accountability processes

Having established standard work and visual representations of progress, there is then a need for a process to tackle the problems that this reveals. Hence the team established daily morning meetings. Each supervisor meets with their team at the start of each shift to review problems encountered in the previous 24 hours and set a plan for the shift's activities. It is up to the team (not the supervisor) to identify and test out counter measures to the problems that are identified.

Only where there are issues that are agreed to be beyond the team's immediate control does the supervisor have a responsibility to take these away and act on them. The team leaders from the different teams then hold a daily supervisors' meeting to reflect on the issues that have come out from their morning meetings with their staff. It is at these that cross-cutting issues are discussed and issues that are of wider significance to the Trust elevated to the next level of management.

These daily accountability processes have built the foundation skills necessary for the sustainability of lean as a daily activity. They have enabled the team leaders to set goals and monitor performance. They have also allowed them to coach and develop their staff in a way that simply isn't possible if problems are only being surfaced and addressed at large scale monthly meetings with multipoint agendas.

The daily accountability processes have encouraged staff to come up with their own improvement ideas and allowed for direct real time feedback on these. They have simplified and streamlined the work of the team leaders and related it more closely to the reality of how well the processes which their team are operating are actually performing. Because communication has been daily and feedback immediate it has been more difficult for resentments or misunderstandings to build up and cause longer term underlying problems.

Training

The training of staff has been a critical element in establishing the blood science laboratories daily lean management system. This has been not only to teach tools and methods but to instil a lean mindset. The training has included broad awareness raising sessions. Some of these have been led by the Chief Executive or other Directors who have presented the overall vision for the Trust and shown how a lean blood sciences laboratory is contributing to the bigger picture. Other sessions have provided a basic introduction to lean.

Much of the training has been delivered by staff directly involved in BICS both from within pathology and also from other departments. This has been far more effective than bringing in external consultants or trainers to deliver this type of training. The credibility factor is greatly increased when staff hear someone present the picture who is regarded as 'one of us' and who can see the potential problems and pitfalls with the approach as well as the advantages.

Visits to other lean organisations have also proved fruitful in raising awareness of the potential of the approach. Indeed staff have talked about visits to BAE systems and other local factories as being 'a revelation'. Seeing lean in practice on the ground and talking to shop floor operators has been far more powerful than attending lectures or reading academic texts.

In addition to these awareness-raising sessions, training has been provided in the tools and techniques. This has included the daily application of methods such as root cause analysis, for example using fishbone diagrams or 5 Whys. Training has also involved the participation of staff in lean events, both within pathology and within the hospital generally. By the end of 2007, 34% of the staff in the Blood Sciences Laboratory had taken part in at least one week long rapid improvement event. Many had done multiple events and were on the way to becoming considerably more expert in the application of lean tools and techniques than those who are managing them!

Discipline and determination

None of this would have been possible without the resilience of the pathology management team and their persistence in the face of repeated setbacks. Winston Churchill is reputed to have defined success as 'the ability to move from one failure to another without any perceptible loss of momentum'. The Pathology Department manager described the lean transformation of the blood sciences laboratory as 'like running down hill. It's exhilarating and terrifying at the same time. You can make a lot of rapid progress but always run the risk of falling flat on your face'.

Although the pathology team have moved a long way from where they started one of the critical insights in a lean transformation is that whenever you reach one level you quickly become dissatisfied and wish to reach the next. Consequently the team are already becoming disenchanted with their progress and want to embed lean further still to improve their processes, eliminate defects and provide a better service to their customers.

As a result of what Pathology have achieved many staff from other parts of the hospital are now visiting the blood sciences laboratory to see at first hand lean in action on a daily basis. This is a small step towards embedding lean in the DNA of the hospital as a whole. But no journey can begin without that all important first step being taken.

References
1. Mann, D. (2005) *Creating a Lean Culture*, New York: Productivity Press.

Chapter Eleven

Supporting a lean healthcare transformation

SUMMARY

- Frontline lean improvement activity is the engine which drives transformation;

- Operational support mechanisms need to be put in place at a hospital wide level;

- At a health community level a strategic approach to lean healthcare can pay significant dividends;

- Lean operational support includes:
  - Investment in developing skills and capabilities
  - Creating a hospital wide lean support function including lean expertise and facilitation skills
  - Establishing human resources policies and priorities to support lean improvement
  - Developing a new approach to leadership, management and coaching which is not typically found in a healthcare setting.

Early in 2006, Bolton Hospital developed a five-year vision for the development of lean healthcare. We have since come to realise that this was probably too short a timescale! Evidence from other sectors is that it takes at least this long to adapt the tools and techniques of lean in to a new setting. However, the underpinning cultural transformation which organisations need to undergo to become truly lean can take as many as twenty years so a much longer-term perspective is needed.

The framework which we developed recognises that there are three different levels of lean activity as indicated in the diagram overleaf.

Lean improvement

As typical MBA trained managers we originally drew this diagram the other way up! There is a natural tendency to begin with strategy and then cascade that throughout the organisation in the hope that it eventually reaches those staff in direct contact with

Figure 26: A different approach to Lean

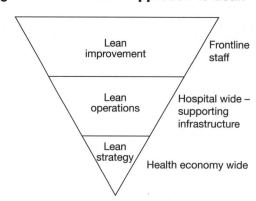

customers on a day to day basis. We quickly came to realise that lean required a different approach.

Hospitals and healthcare systems attempting a lean transformation are best advised to start by establishing the habits and disciplines of lean improvement at the frontline. Textbooks and conferences can provide a theoretical understanding of lean concepts but it is only by experiencing them in practice that you come to realise their full potential. It is also the case that lean places a strong emphasis on going to the 'gemba' i.e. the place where the work is actually done.

All too often Boards of Directors develop strategies in splendid isolation from the day to day realities faced by frontline staff and the patients and families that they serve. As a consequence our model for achieving a lean healthcare transformation starts with frontline lean improvement. This is the place where our most intensive early effort has been put to raise awareness, develop skills and deliver early results that will build the momentum towards a wider transformation.

Many organisations will never proceed beyond this phase. Point Kaizen activity in individual departments or even flow Kaizen activity across whole patient journeys create a feel good factor and can deliver some significant improvements. The challenge is to connect these together in to a genuine and far reaching lean transformation. To achieve this the next two levels in the model are needed.

Lean operations

Lean operations is the recognition that there are cross-cutting hospital wide issues that need to be tackled if incremental improvements are to add up to a wholesale transformation. The elements of the lean operations framework developed in Bolton are the main substance of this chapter.

Lean strategy

The final level of our inverted pyramid is that of lean strategy. By this we mean a coherent health community wide vision which goes beyond the hospital to encompass primary care, community services, social care, the voluntary sector and self care and treatment by patients themselves. This is a difficult undertaking and as a consequence still in its infancy. Success in this area will depend on engaging many partners who will each have their own aims, aspirations and improvement methodologies. However the potential for benefit, both in terms of improved healthcare services and improved health, is enormous.

Just imagine if we had an effective lean way of encouraging citizens to adopt healthier lifestyles, reduce obesity and excess alcohol consumption, promote exercise and engage early in preventative medicine. When viewed in this way, the patient journey really starts with a healthy citizen. Effective interventions at the beginning of this journey in terms of health promotion and disease prevention could eliminate huge amounts of waste and non-value added activity in terms of the burden of disease, ill health and disability. When thought of in this way then those who plan and commission healthcare services such as primary care trusts in the UK, municipal authorities, governments and insurers in other systems should be showing a great deal more interest than they are in how lean thinking could support the improvement of health and healthcare for their citizens.

This is a topic which is probably worthy of a whole book in its own right. In Bolton we are beginning to take early steps towards this by discussing the work that we have been doing using lean with our partners such as Bolton Primary Care Trust and Bolton Metropolitan Borough Council to explore ways in which we can work together to realise wider benefits for local people. For now let's concentrate on what can be done to create a lean operating infrastructure at the hospital level.

The BICS model

The BICS model was described in detail in Section Two of this book. That description focused on using lean methodology to bring about improvements by working through repeated PDCA cycles. The full model makes explicit the supporting infrastructure that is needed as shown in the diagram overleaf.

Developing skills and capabilities

The majority of healthcare staff including managers have often had little formal training in problem solving methods or in quality improvement tools and techniques. The added value of a lean perspective, including the identification and elimination of waste, is something which even fewer possess. Anyone attempting a lean healthcare transformation therefore needs to invest heavily in developing the knowledge, skills and capabilities of staff.

Figure 27: The Bolton Improving Care System (BICS)

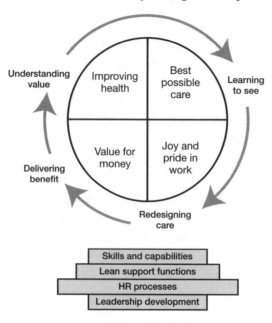

Toyota themselves are again the gold standard in this. Over many years they have developed intensive on and off the job training programmes. Their induction for all new starters at any level in the company is lengthy and in great depth. Progression through the organisation depends not just on technical know how but also on a mastery of the Toyota philosophy and a rigorous approach to problem solving. This is something which Toyota have developed over decades. Establishing it from scratch is no mean feat!

Within healthcare there is at least a healthy respect for the concept of professional development. Most of those who work in healthcare have a disposition to learn and are keen to take on board new knowledge and skills providing they can be assured of its relevance to their day to day work. A variety of training and development vehicles have been used in Bolton to establish basic understanding and to deepen skills and capabilities. These have included:

- **Induction** – at the day long corporate induction experienced by all new starters, there is a session on the aims and values of the hospital and the basics of BICS approach are explained. This session is led either by the Chief Executive or in his absence by an Executive Director.

- **Awareness sessions** – BICS awareness sessions are run on a regular basis. These involve presentations from frontline staff who have themselves been involved in lean activity to achieve peer to peer spread of knowledge and skills.

- **One off training in tools and techniques** – some departments within the Trust have found it helpful to run special sessions on particular techniques to ensure that there is consistency of application, especially if these are to be used on a day to day basis.

- **Visits, conferences and reading** – visits to external organisations have proved particularly useful. Whilst a great deal can be learned from listening to conference speeches or reading about lean concepts, it is far more powerful to see it in action. Furthermore the experience of going off site and visiting a factory or a military base is a stimulus to staff to reframe their thinking.

- **BICS events** – these are invaluable in the development of skills and capabilities. There is simply no substitute for learning the tools 'live' on the job. It allows staff to move quickly from an academic appreciation into a practical application. It shows the immediate relevance and the potential benefit for improving care and making working life easier. The success of this approach depends on effective facilitation from the BICS team and support from our external Simpler sensei to ensure that tools and techniques are taught at an appropriate time and to a consistent standard.

- **Leadership programme** – over the last two years we have developed a leadership programme for our most senior managerial and clinical leaders in the Trust and have run leadership events for frontline leaders. These all include exposure to lean methodology. I will return to the importance of leadership development in more detail towards the end of this chapter.

- **Graduated curriculum in lean expertise** – despite all of these initiatives and mechanisms for developing skills and capabilities it is clear that we need to raise our game. If the hospital is to undergo a fundamental lean transformation then every employee needs to have a lean mindset and an appropriate level of expertise in the approach.

  Consequently we have been working with our consulting partners, Simpler, to develop a graduated curriculum whereby all 3,500 members of staff will receive accredited training in the BICS approach. Levels of attainment will range green through to platinum.

  All staff will receive mandatory training to the green level. Those wanting to progress to a first line supervisory position will be expected to achieve a bronze accreditation whilst those in senior middle management positions will be expected to achieve silver. At this level there will be a requirement to successfully complete a two week programme which will include both off the job learning and participation in lean improvement activities.

  Those who aspire to reach director level or to become members of the central BICS team will be expected to train to the gold standard. The notion of a platinum standard is a relatively late addition. This is getting close to sensei level and it may well be some time before any of our own in house team attain this lofty goal!

  A schematic setting out the framework and some of the emerging content is shown overleaf. This approach is a genuine partnership between Bolton Hospital and Simpler Consulting with Bolton providing the healthcare insights and Simpler the lean expertise.

Figure 28: Bolton Hospital – Simpler Healthcare™ Certification

	Green	Bronze	Silver	Gold	Platinum
	3 hours	3 days	2 weeks	2 weeks	3 days
Prerequisites	None	Green certification / Advanced reading	Bronze certification / Advanced reading	Silver certification / Advanced reading	Gold certification
Knowledge	Business case; History of lean; Fundamentals of BICS; Flow game; Journey update Thedacare video; Journey update pathology video	Effective team management; Bolton management system (BICS); A3 thinking; RIE preparation RIE event RIE sustainment; Problem solving and CA tools; Team leader training; Certification assessment	VSA methodology; VSA scoping; 6S and visual management; One need flow; Pull systems; Standard work; Flow cell basic tools	Policy deployment; 2P/3P; Product/service development; Project management; Leadership and followership; Steering Committee	Mentorships; Partnerships; TPOC/mission sponsorship; Facilitation/coaching
Skills	Understand Bolton's commitment to patient care; Understand the history of continuous improvement; Understand how I can learn and contribute	Understand each role as it relates to BICS; How to use A3 thinking to solve problems; Understand your role in team participation and event management	How to select key areas for targeted improvement; How to use basic tools to see and eliminate waste; How to lead others in the application of the methods	How to link improvement to strategy; How to use advanced tools when and where appropriate; Understand how to develop the BICS infrastructure	How to apply transformational thinking; How to apply the technique for each respective tool; The ability to mentor the application of BICS at all levels
Behaviours	Can describe the high level BICS approach; Can describe why BICS is important	Using A3 thinking to solve problems; Seeing elements of waste	Working effectively in a team; Identifying process problems before people problems	Leading improvement in a systematic way; Working with complexity (people, process and tools)	Unquestionable belief that the tools apply everywhere; Confidence to teach others at any level
Requirements	Green certificate	Bronze training certificate; Participate in one PS/CA activity**	Silver training certificate; Participate in one VSA activity; Participate in two RIEs**	Gold training certificate; Lead one VSA activity; Lead 2 RIEs**	Platinum certificate; Participated/lead 20+ RIEs; Developed 3 mission A3s

Process → Capability → Culture → Results

**Must demonstrate proper preparation, execution and sustainment using A3 methodology

Creating hospital-wide lean support functions

Bolton Hospital's Facilities Division encompasses non-clinical support services. These include areas such the laundry, estates department, equipment sterilisation unit, portering, cleaning and catering. There are many unsung heroes who work in these areas. They carry out tasks which patients and the general public often don't even know about. This includes many difficult and unpleasant jobs which are at the essential but unglamorous end of healthcare delivery. The General Manager in-charge of this area is an enthusiastic lean convert. He has described visiting the Toyota plant in Derby UK as 'a revelation'. His determination to create the first lean facilities set up in a UK hospital is infectious.

This manager has made a presentation to literally hundreds of his staff which begins with a photograph of a high jumper sailing over the bar backwards. This is the famous Dick Fosbery. Up until the 1968 Olympics everyone had run towards the high jump bar face on and jumped over it pretty well head first. Dick Fosbery broke the mould. He firstly drew amusement and ridicule and then admiration when he turned backwards to leap over the bar setting a new world record in the process. Nobody had done it that way before but it proved to be highly effective. Slowly over time it has become the norm for all successful high jumpers. There is a wonderful metaphor here for lean healthcare pioneers. What is being attempted may well look ungainly but if it succeeds it will raise the bar for everyone and in time may well become the norm.

It is significant that lean is taking hold in these parts of the hospital. One of the essential features of lean is uncovering hidden processes and hence hidden problems and waste. Many support functions are in parts of the hospital which remain unseen by clinical staff. But unless they also take a lean approach and support the development of lean healthcare then we won't achieve an overall transformation of the hospital.

There are two types of support functions. Firstly, those which provide services directly to frontline staff and patients; secondly those which provide information or expertise to support the process of lean transformation. The first category are the more obvious and easy to deal with. They include functions such as the provision of clean linen, wholesome and appetising food, hygienic and well maintained wards and clinics. Inevitably there is a great deal of waste in these processes just as there is within the clinical processes in healthcare. Indeed because some functions such as equipment sterilisation or the laundry more closely resemble manufacturing environments it is easier to make a direct translation of lean tools and techniques in to these areas.

The laundry is an excellent case in point. Housed in a Victorian building it is hot, dirty and unpleasant work. Most UK hospitals have put their laundry services out to tender and linen is now most usually laundered by a private sector provider who seeks economies of scale through large centralised laundry facilities. In 2005, the intention was to 'market test' the laundry service in Bolton in just this way but the laundry manager, with the full support of the local trade unions, said 'if lean is so good why not let us use it on the laundry to strengthen our own in house bid'.

It was hard to resist such logic! The laundry staff took to the lean approach with great enthusiasm. Within just a few short months the environment was much cleaner, tidier and safer. Old pieces of machinery which had lain dormant for many years were moved out and disposed of as scrap. Processes were streamlined and flow established. The results were dramatic and included floor space savings, workforce productivity improvements and a significant financial gain at the bottom line. This retained the laundry service in house. What is more the savings generated more than paid for the total cash outlay on management consultancy for the first two years of the lean transformation programme.

Our early work in Bolton showed that lean can deliver results in very different kinds of processes – whether the aim be reduced trauma mortality or more efficient linen services. This was a powerful lesson. Progressively other support services are being improved using lean methodology.

The information technology help desk for example has looked at the statistics on the calls it most frequently receives by category and by area of the Trust and has redesigned its processes to make responses quicker and more effective. It is now getting upstream and developing a preventative approach to train IT users so that the most common requests for help can be dealt with without recourse to the central team.

Similarly the estates department have reviewed the way in which they respond to maintenance requests and re-profiled staffing levels and work patterns to better match their capacity to the demand. The use of lean tools to review the way in which estates staff move around the hospital has helped to remove unnecessary steps (literally!) and to save time which can be reinvested in preventative maintenance. The human resources and finance functions are also looking at how their own processes can be improved through a lean approach, for example, to speed up the requisition and purchase process or to improve the ease of recruiting staff.

There are a second category of lean support functions which are needed to support a transformation. These are those which are required to support the lean improvement effort itself. The most prominent example in Bolton is the BICS team. This was previously a service development team which had some knowledge of quality improvement techniques and which responded to requests for help from various parts of the hospital. This team had always been skilled and enthusiastic, but had never before had a strategic context for its work.

Although relatively small in number, the BICS team have been essential to the work that has been carried out in Bolton so far. Their own learning curve has been steep but with the help and support of our Simpler sensei and lean practitioners from other organisations, they have rapidly developed their skills and understanding.

They need not only a working knowledge of lean tools and techniques but also strong facilitation skills and project management capabilities to ensure that the seven week cycles of VSAs and rapid improvement events are well managed. This includes the preparation and follow up stages as well as during event weeks themselves.

The main difficulty for the team to date is that it simply isn't extensive enough. At the time of writing we are in the process of doubling the size of the team from five staff to ten. We are doing this by seconding in staff from the operating divisions of the hospital. The deal is that they will spend the next twelve months becoming immersed in lean tools and techniques and supporting improvement activity. They will then return to their divisions with the remit to bring their lean knowledge to bear in an operational role. Our goal is to continue to double the size of the team year on year for at least the next three years in order to support the progressive transformation of the hospital.

In addition to the BICS team themselves there are a number of other central support functions which have proved invaluable in establishing the BICS approach. These include the information department – producing detailed analysis of workload and capacity and teaching others the skills of information analysis and presentation; the clinical effectiveness team who are a prime source of information and inspiration in relation to evidence based practice – the bedrock for standard work; the HR and organisational development team who assist with the change management aspects of lean events; and the finance team who work to track the benefits including the financial gains which result from our lean improvement efforts.

Establishing effective human resources processes

A lean transformation means great changes for staff within the organisation. Inevitably not everyone sees this as positive. There will be a range of legitimate concerns from staff and trade unions about the impact on job security and working lives. Consequently a strong framework of human resources processes is essential. A good working partnerships with staff and staff side representatives is one of the mainstays of any lean effort.

In Bolton Hospital we are lucky in having high quality staff representatives drawn from a wide range of trade unions and professional associations. Without exception they are strongly committed to the NHS and to the future of the hospital and want to see it do well. But inevitably they are somewhat wary of a lean approach. They have all heard the catch phrases such as 'lean and mean' and initially assume that the application of such methods is about penny pinching and making do with less. Underlying these concerns which may be based upon misapprehension are a range of legitimate worries which need to be addressed. These include:

- **Does lean mean fewer jobs?**
  It is certainly true that lean aims to identify waste and activity that doesn't add value. The goal is to redesign work so that staff spend more of their time on activity that directly adds value to the customer. In some cases this might mean that less staff are needed to complete a particular activity. If staff are to be motivated to become involved in lean redesign work then it is absolutely essential that a strong commitment is given that no-one will lose their job as a result of doing so.

  Within Bolton an agreement has been reached with staff side representatives which indicates that where lean enables an activity to be completed with fewer staff those staff will be redeployed either on to new work that brings in new income, or in to vacancies elsewhere in the department or elsewhere in the hospital, or full time on to quality improvement work. This is not to say that hospitals don't need to make savings, many do. In Bolton this has meant fewer numbers of jobs but this has been achieved by not replacing staff as they leave through natural turnover. Staff who are freed up by BICS activity can then be redeployed in to vacancies as they arise.

- **Will change be imposed from outside?**

  The whole emphasis on lean redesign is that it is led by those who are the experts i.e. the staff actually doing the work for themselves. If a lean redesign is imposed from outside by a service improvement team, or worse still by management consultants, its chance of long term sustainability is slim.

- **Are staff being regimented and standardised?**

  Sometimes staff representatives are concerned that the kind of measures developed during rapid improvement events such as takt time are a return to the old days of time and motion studies. It is essential to convince staff and their representatives that this is not the case. If we can see that there is a best way of doing things then it must make sense to encourage everyone to do it that way! Furthermore standardising work and only carrying out those tasks that are absolutely necessary, frees staff to spend more time on the creative discretionary elements of their job that are the most fulfilling.

- **Do rapid improvement events allow inadequate time for consultation?**

  To some extent this can be problematic, which is why choosing the right topic for a rapid improvement event is essential. It is also essential to consult and discuss the changes proposed in a rapid improvement event with staff and staff side representatives as the event week progresses. If it becomes clear that there is a major 'show stopper' then it may be better to pilot it during the week and to implement it following detailed discussions or negotiations with staff and their representatives. This however is rare and it is almost always the case that if staff can see during a rapid improvement event week that something works well from the point of view of patients and staff, then everyone is happy to maintain it following the RIE.

- **If cost savings are to be made, how will those savings be applied?**

  In the UK healthcare organisations within the public sector are not commercial profit making businesses. As a consequence any savings generated do not go in to the pockets of shareholders or owners. They are available for reinvesting in improvements to the quality of patient care.

  We have found that it is helpful to have regular discussions and joint meetings with staff side representatives. This happens both through our normal consultative forums but also by having staff representatives present on our BICS development forum that engages a range of stakeholders. Staff side representatives have also been trained in the BICS methodology and taken part in a lean event.

  We also work to emphasise to staff and staff side representatives the benefits of BICS, both for staff and for the patients. This doesn't mean that problems never arise. For example, staff side representatives have expressed concerns on occasions about teams of staff travelling overseas to understand how lean works in other settings such as in Thedacare Hospital in Wisconsin. The key is to maintain integrity and respect in the relationship, to be honest with each other about aspirations and concerns and to maintain a shared vision and goal of better patient care and improving working lives for the staff delivering it.

Developing a new approach to leadership

I recently heard a presentation at a major conference on lean from an ex-Toyota Executive. David Verble worked for Toyota in North America for fourteen years. His role was as a change agent responsible for bringing the skills and knowledge of Toyota's systems and practices to American executives and managers. David recounted his surprise on joining Toyota at the style of management and leadership he encountered. As he put it 'you can never get anyone to give you a direct answer!' (1).

In most organisations workers are used to elevating problems to their bosses and then blaming them when they don't get resolved. In Toyota the problem would be bounced straight back. A supervisor almost always answers a question or concern from an employee with a string of further questions. This is part of the Toyota philosophy that the best way of motivating people is to allow them to take responsibility for their own area of work and for solving their own problems themselves. David Verble referred to this approach in Toyota as PDCA for People Development.

Mr Cho who is now Chairman of the Toyota group was reputed to define the Toyota style of leadership as being:

1. Give him or her the job
2. Let them think, let them try
3. Help him or her see
4. Force reflection

In un-Toyota like organisations – which I would guess includes most hospitals and other healthcare establishments – this approach would be as counter-cultural to staff as it would to their supervisors. Supervisors are used to giving instructions and having them followed even if only perfunctorily. Employees are used to elevating their problems upwards and come to accept that they rarely get satisfactory answers.

A framework which I have found helps in thinking differently about management and leadership is that developed in Myles Downey's excellent book, Effective Coaching (2). Downey uses the following model to distinguish between the different roles of management, leadership and coaching (see overleaf).

The most commonly found set of behaviours within organisations are those which relate to **management**. These include setting out what is expected of employees, issuing instructions, allocating tasks and checking that they have been completed.

Less common but still found in effective organisations is the role of **leadership**. This involves answering the 'why' question. Helping give workers meaning and purpose in their work by showing them how their own role contributes to the bigger mission of the enterprise.

Figure 29: Leadership–coaching–management framework

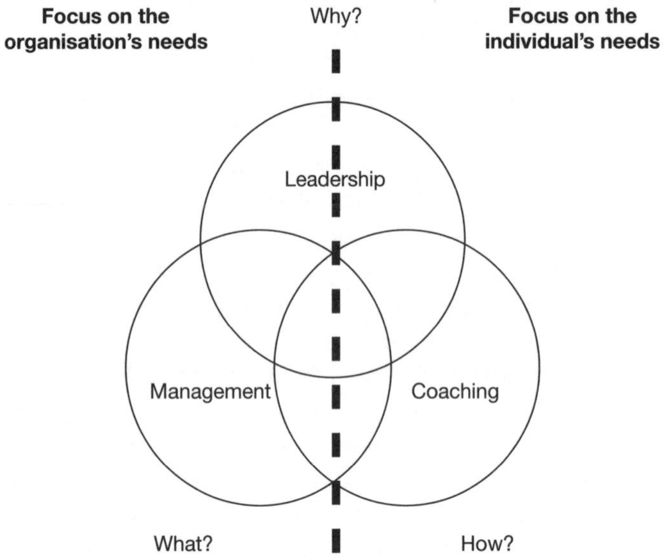

(Adapted from Myles Downey 'Effective Coaching')

The least common of the three is the role of **coaching**. This is about how an individual conducts his or her job. This is mainly within the discretion of the individual. The role of the coach is to enable the individual to perform his or her tasks better by helping them fulfil their true potential.

In an effective organisation supervisors will adopt all three types of roles at the appropriate times. Indeed knowing when to move in and out of each role is essential. There is no point adopting a non-directive coaching style with a new employee who doesn't understand what is expected of them and who needs direct guidance, instruction and support.

Downey suggests that different types of behaviours are needed for the three different roles:

- **leadership**
  - conversations about organisational mission, vision, goals and values
  - role modelling behaviours and values
  - inspiring and motivating
- **management**
  - appraisals
  - setting individual and departmental goals
  - recruitment interviews
  - creating personal development plans
  - agreeing parameters of projects, tasks, disciplinary meetings

- **coaching**
  - conversations about how to deliver goals, plans etc.
  - giving feedback, making suggestions, offering advice
  - on the job training

Those in leadership positions need to learn the behaviours and skills of all three roles and become adept at distinguishing when is the correct time to use a particular approach.

The skills of coaching do not come naturally to most managers (I speak as someone who has tried to learn and apply them!). To be an effective coach in the workplace the supervisor must resist the temptation to immediately give the employee what he or she sees as 'the answer'. Instead it is important to develop a non-directive style. People are perfectly capable of working out answers for themselves and of developing their own plan to improve their performance if only they are given the responsibility and encouragement.

Some of the core skills which need to be learned in adopting a coaching role include:

- generating understanding – helping the person being coached to better understand themselves or to understand their situation so that they can make better decisions
- proposing – making available to the person being coached some of the coach's experience and insights. This should be done carefully and with the coachee's agreement or else otherwise the coach runs the risk of simply 'telling'
- asking open questions – it is enlightening how a series of open questions can enable the individual being coached to probe more deeply in to their own concerns, motivations and fears and develop a plan for dealing with these. This is almost exactly the same techniques as the five whys used in problem solving
- summarising – playing back to the person being coached a summary of what they have said helps them to affirm thoughts that may have previously been lacking coherence or structure. It also shows them they are being listened to which can be something of a novelty in the workplace!

This coaching role is firmly embedded in the Toyota way of doing things. I believe that it is an essential pre-requisite for any organisation wishing to become truly lean.

Making a shift from this directive style of management which currently exists in most of our workplaces to a more sophisticated approach which keeps responsibility with each individual employee is quite a challenge! In Bolton we have been edging towards this through the way in which we have developed our leadership programmes. The first of these has been for senior managerial and clinical leaders in the hospital. It has contained training in tools and techniques of a lean approach and also in the skills of leadership, management and coaching. It has involved personality questionnaires and 360° feedback to give individuals greater insight and self awareness. Finally, it has provided the opportunity to practice these skills in live situations and receive feedback.

A similar programme has just been run for fifty further clinical leaders in the Trust from a cross-section of professional backgrounds who are in less senior leadership positions and a new programme for first level leaders is currently in development. This will become an integral part of the Trust's graduated curriculum in the BICS approach as it is finalised and rolled out. We are presently reflecting on how we can build on this to achieve a more rapid move towards a coaching culture.

So these four elements, developing skills and capabilities, creating lean support functions, establishing effective human resources processes and developing a new approach to management are fundamental underpinnings to a lean healthcare transformation. They are evidence for the supposition that creating a lean organisation is at least as much about organisational development as it is about the application of quality improvement tools and techniques. To paraphrase what the ex-U.S. President Bill Clinton once said during an election campaign 'it's the people stupid'. This is true in any lean transformation. In healthcare people (healthcare staff) deal with other people (patients and their families) at the most vulnerable and emotionally intense time of their lives. So getting the human dimensions right is of fundamental importance.

References

1. Verble, D. (2007) Presentation to Australasia Redesigning Healthcare Summit, Sydney, February.
2. Downey, M. (2003) *Effective Coaching*, Mason, OH: Texere.

Chapter Twelve

Reflections

SUMMARY

- Reflection and learning are a critical part of a successful lean transformation;

- Change is difficult; a lean transformation in healthcare is especially difficult due to its pioneering nature and the cultural barriers to be overcome;

- Leaders who are embarking on a lean healthcare journey must be prepared for challenges and setbacks. These can be overcome by:
  - Understanding people's motivations and fears
  - Reflecting on mistakes made and learning lessons
  - Having a model for managing change
  - Drawing strength from colleagues and supporters and from within yourself;

- The benefits to patients and the enthusiasm of staff provide ample motivation and encouragement in troubled times.

The Japanese have a word called hansei. It can be loosely translated as reflection although this doesn't really do it justice. For the Japanese, hansei is a mindset or an attitude. It means scrutinising carefully what you have done and identifying weaknesses or areas of improvement. Without hansei there can be no kaizen or continuous improvement. The other way to think about this is that hansei is the check part of the plan, do, check, adjust, cycle.

In my experience reflection is something which western organisations rarely do. In fact a lot of improvement activity feels like repeated cycles of plan…do…plan… do…plan…do…plan…do There is little checking and learning and so the adjustments that are needed to lift improvement to a new level are never made. When understood in this way reflection is a critical part of any successful lean transformation. It needs to be applied not only to the service challenges you face, but also to the process of improvement itself. Anyone who is embarking on a lean transformation, whether they be a departmental manager or a chief executive, would do well to create the time and space that will be needed for reflection and learning. So I felt that the concluding chapter of this book should include some personal hansei – my reflections on what has been difficult, and what could have been improved during the first steps on my own lean journey.

The challenge that lean leaders face

Imagine that you are a superintendent radiographer running a twenty-person department in a busy general hospital. Having recently been to a conference and heard about the benefits of lean, you are keen to try the approach out in your own department. So at the next departmental meeting you gather everyone together, radiographers, doctors, administrative staff and make a short and enthusiastic speech about how the problems which the department is facing – long waiting times, piles of unreported x-rays, overworked and harassed staff – can be solved by a lean approach. What kind of reaction do you think you might get? Here are some of the things I expect your team might say:

- 'We're not Japanese and we don't make cars'
- 'The problems aren't our fault'
- 'This sounds all very well but we are too busy to do this'
- 'Doesn't the hospital have a quality improvement team, surely it's their job?'
- 'We can't mess about with this, we've got targets to hit'.

What may not be said but which many may be thinking, even the silent majority, is 'this will go away in a month or two when she attends another conference and finds out about an even newer fad, let's just sit this one out'.

If you are a Chief Executive rather than a departmental manager you can at least exercise your positional power. You can push hard to get the issue on agendas and insist on some pilots being run. You can find a few people to take part in lean activities even if you can't force them to be enthusiastic about it. If you want to embark on a lean transformation from within the middle of the healthcare organisation it can be a lot more difficult. I recently met a radiologist who had learned about lean whilst studying for an MBA. Quietly and doggedly she had set about transforming her ultrasound department. This had taken her years not months and she had done it with no apparent support or appreciation from anyone else in her organisation. The results were spectacular and she had delivered them despite the odds.

A more common reaction in such a situation is to lose belief in yourself and in the ideas you are promoting. It's easy to talk yourself in to thinking 'lean probably does have a lot of advantages but now isn't the right time to try it'. So from my own personal experience over a two year period of dealing with these challenges, what is the best way to overcome them and what are important mistakes to avoid?

My reflections are that aspiring lean leaders need to:

- Understand peoples' motivations and fears
- Continually reflect on mistakes made and learn lessons from them
- Develop a personal model for managing change
- Draw strength from colleagues, supporters and from within yourself.

Understanding people's motivations and fears

It is a mistake to think that everyone will be well disposed towards new initiatives. Others aren't always willing to embrace a lean approach just because you yourself have been converted. Equally it is unduly pessimistic to assume that everyone is always cynical and dismissive. You need to understand the balance between these extremes within your own team or organisation and develop appropriate strategies for those different motivations and concerns.

There are numerous psychological tools that can be used to profile how willingly people will accept new ideas and practices. One of the best known is the diffusion theory of change developed by William Rogers. This assumes that people fall along a spectrum from innovators to laggards (1) The following diagram is adapted from Rogers' work:

Figure 30: Rogers' diffusion theory model

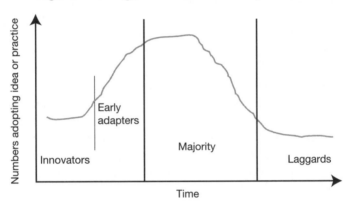

There is a risk that this is overly simplistic. There may be individuals who are capable of great ingenuity and original thinking but who have become so disaffected that this is hidden under a blanket of apparent cynicism. To help myself understand these issues better I have developed a simple two by two grid. It would be nice to claim that this was drawn up on the basis of extensive scientific research. In actual fact it was a doodle on the margins of an agenda paper when I was trying in a long and difficult meeting to gain an understanding of why some of my clinical colleagues didn't share my own enthusiasm for the latest new ideas! I refer to it as Fillingham's Motivational Matrix (see overleaf).

Those in the bottom right hand quadrant are the **embittered cynics**. It's often assumed that there are many of these working in hospitals. My own experience is that true cynics are a very small minority indeed. The reason for their embitterment might be their underlying personality or traumatic events that have happened to them in their life or their career. Whatever the cause, changing their outlook and behaviour is certainly an uphill struggle. 'We tried it that way in 1993, it didn't work then and wont now' is an often heard response from this group. They aren't really interested in the facts of the situation and no amount of data will convince them that they are part of the prob-

Figure 31: Fillingham's motivational matrix

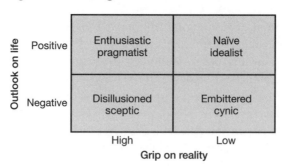

lem and could be part of a creative solution. Organisations with too high numbers of embittered cynics are unlikely to survive in the long run. Difficult though it may be they need to be encouraged to pursue their career development elsewhere.

I believe that far more common in healthcare organisations are those in the bottom left hand box, the **disillusioned sceptics**. These are people who have a negative outlook on life not because they don't know what's going on but because they do know what's going on! These include doctors, nurses, therapists and other frontline staff in our wards, clinics and departments who every day see the countless errors, delays, frustrations and unresolved problems that prevent the delivery of good quality care to patients. The sad thing is that when these staff embarked on their careers in healthcare, they were often in the top right hand box, the naïve idealists. They wanted a career helping people and doing good but during their training and their early years in work they came to realise that no matter how hard they tried, the system seemed to conspire against them. All too often the outcomes and experience of patients fell far short of that which they wanted to see. It's little wonder that disillusionment creeps in as the problems with the current reality become clear.

Naïve idealists are those with optimism, but little understanding of day to day realities. Sadly many quality improvers are often seen as belonging to this group. They use rhetoric and good intentions rather than data and evidence to try to convince their colleagues that methodologies such as lean really can make a difference. This is unlikely to convert the sceptics and will provoke outright hostility from the cynics.

The challenge for an aspiring lean leader is to discover those prized individuals who are in the top left hand box, the **enthusiastic pragmatists**. These are that rare breed, who can look the problems square in the face and not be daunted by them. They understand that things aren't as they should be but use this as the impetus to seek improvement. A tiny smattering of these individuals can quickly infect others and generate positive change. The way to pull more people in to the enthusiastic pragmatists camp is by showing them the evidence. Collect data on the current state, use evidence based techniques to bring about improvements and show that these can be sustained through robust and credible reporting.

This enthusiastic pragmatist approach is what Jim Collins has called the 'Honesty/ Faith Paradox'. Jim Collins wrote a book called 'Good to Great' in which he showed how many leading commercial organisations made the transformation from being merely average in their industry sectors, to outstanding performance (2). This had often taken them a decade or longer. One of the common characteristics which all of them showed was that they were brutally honest about the facts of their own position. They never claimed to be good when they weren't and they brought an intense spotlight of scrutiny to bear upon their weaknesses and deficiencies.

They didn't let this honest appraisal depress them. Rather than becoming gloomy and giving up (as all too often happens in healthcare) they kept on being optimistic and believing that if only they worked together, one day they would solve their problems and make the leap to greatness. This honesty/faith paradox – balancing an open acceptance of what isn't working with a driven determination to change it is at the heart of enthusiastic pragmatism. Its the key to converting the sceptics and building momentum behind any lean transformation.

Reflecting on mistakes and learning lessons

One of the great strengths of Toyota is that they are continually looking for their problems, weaknesses and mistakes. To outsiders this can appear intensely self-critical and overly focused on the negative. If this were true it would be a concern as research by organisational psychologists has shown that people produce better results when they feel good about themselves. But it needs to be understood that intense reflection and self criticism in an effort to bring about improvement are part of Japanese culture in a way in which they are not a feature of most western societies.

Anyone embarking on a lean transformation needs to develop this ability to reflect and learn. There is often as much, if not more, to be gleaned from what doesn't go well as from what does. The pace of improvement can be greatly speeded up by careful reflection and intelligent application of the lessons learned.

During our two year lean journey in Bolton we have made many mistakes. The tips and advice presented in Section Two of this book have grown out of an extensive period of trial and error – a continuing series of PDCA cycles. As well as practical advice on applying the tools, techniques and methods of lean healthcare, there are a number of more general reflections which I think are pertinent to those leading a lean healthcare transformation. These apply equally well whether you are seeking to redesign a single department or an entire healthcare system.

Our biggest lessons have been:

- **Claiming victory too early**. There is a natural tendency in improvement efforts to want to celebrate success. This is a good instinct. It is important to praise the achievements of those who have shown courage and ingenuity to bring about change. Delivering and publicising early wins is an essential component of an effective change strategy. It is however essential to maintain a careful balance between building momentum and over-claiming for the successes that have been delivered.

Anyone who claims to have created a lean hospital or even a lean department after just a few rapid improvement events is almost certainly deluding themselves. Their claims will lack credibility on close inspection. For this reason it is wise to balance publicity around improvements with a genuinely felt reminder that you are still a novice in the field of lean healthcare.

My friend John Toussaint, the CEO of Thedacare, has said, 'when you are only two years old you can't be more than two years old'. There's no use trying to pretend that you are a fully-fledged lean adult when you are still only a toddler! As you progress on your lean journey this becomes increasingly clear. Concepts that at first appeared straightforward take on new layers of meaning and complexity. Any false modesty you may have shown at the outset becomes more genuine as you see what has been achieved in other sectors and understand just how long it will take to achieve the full potential of lean in healthcare.

- **Letting a thousand flowers bloom** – at one time this phrase was popular and seemed to suggest an enlightened enthusiasm for promoting good ideas and initiatives whatever source they come from. There is some sense in this. (In fact an important reflection is that almost all of the 'mistakes' one commits are a question of degree rather than of absolute right or wrong). In any lean healthcare transformation it is important to enlist enthusiasts early on and to foster activity which will deepen an understanding of the lean approach. This is true even if your lean enthusiasts aren't in an area where the need is greatest or where the most dramatic results can be delivered.

  However it's also important to take in to account the opportunity cost involved. In most healthcare organisations staff time is at premium. It isn't easy to free doctors, nurses, therapists and others from busy clinical commitments. Capability in improvement skills is also strictly limited and it is unlikely that you will have an extensive budget to spend on external management consultancy support. As a consequence some form of prioritisation of lean activity is essential.

  In Bolton we have talked about this as striking a balance between 'broad and shallow' and 'narrow and deep'. During our first two years, some of our lean activities have been designed to engage a wide cross-section of staff in different parts of the hospital in departments as diverse as the equipment sterilisation unit, antenatal clinics and the finance department. This is our 'broad and shallow' activity. The rest of our effort has been focussed on high priority areas and particularly on five chosen patient journeys – trauma, cataracts surgery, joint replacements, stroke care and acute abdominal problems. These are our 'narrow and deep' and were chosen either because they were areas of higher than expected mortality or because opportunities existed to reduce waiting times for patients and increase income to the hospital. As we have progressed we have recognised the need to develop a filtering mechanism to agree which topics for improvement should receive the most attention.

- **Lapsing into committee mode** – healthcare organisations like nothing better than a committee or working party! These are often developed to build consensus across a diverse range of professional groups and interests. Unfortunately they can easily descend from an effective means of cooperation to an overly bureaucratic obstacle to progress. Lean methodology is supposed to avoid this trap.

The phrase 'rapid improvement event' sums up the intention – get on with the business of improving patient care as quickly as possible. There is no doubt that the most effective improvement activity is that where staff and patients can see visible change for the better in a short space of time. Our experience is that care is needed to ensure that lean events don't degenerate in to the bad habits of committee style working with a great deal of discussion, often dominated by a few articulate or powerful individuals but little in the way of action.

The key to avoiding this potential pitfall is strong and effective team leadership and facilitation. It is an area where external sensei support can add real value and the development of standard work for team leaders and facilitators is a good means of keeping things on track. Adherence to a well proven methodology – map the current state, envisage the future state, develop an improvement plan – and the consistent application of a few effective techniques are good defenses against an outbreak of 'committee-itus'!

- **Not hurting people's feelings** – because the lean approach looks for problems it often finds them. This can be dispiriting. Most of us are proud of our organisations and it can be discouraging to find that they don't work as well as we had originally imagined. What's more it isn't always easy to get across the message that it is the system of care that is letting patients down rather than the actions of individual members of staff.

  For doctors, nurses, therapists, administrative and support staff who have been struggling to provide the best care that they can within a set of broken processes, it can be the final straw to be told that 'our current state is delivering a poor quality of care'. This can be taken as personal criticism or to imply a lack of professional skill or dedication. Communication and dialogue are essential to overcome this. The active involvement of as many staff as possible who work in a service is critical to getting people to see the need for change in a positive light. Even then it can be an uphill struggle to convince the sceptics that change is needed and that it is not their personal attitude or competence that is being called in to question.

- **Over-exploiting willing volunteers** – there are often a handful of individuals early on in a lean healthcare transformation who become highly enthused and put in a lot of hours over and above their contractual commitment to the lean effort. Without this kind of dedication it is unlikely that any lean transformation would get off the ground. The risk is the tendency to take such individuals for granted. Over-enthusiastic leaders (at any level) can get carried away with their latest idea and not notice that others are struggling to keep up. Because the willing volunteers are such an enthusiastic bunch they don't like to point out that their leader has just proposed the undoable!

The development of effective listening skills and a willingness to take feedback are critical if the leader of a lean transformation is to avoid falling in to the trap of trying to travel too far and too fast. I have personally been sent off to conferences by my own executive team with the express instruction to **NOT** come back with any new ideas or initiatives! Leaders need to keep reminding themselves that they are in a marathon and not a sprint. It is a team event, not a case of pursuing an individual medal.

A model for managing change

A lean healthcare transformation consists of a series of mini transformations. Mastering the technical aspects of process redesign won't by itself deliver results. Only if the process of change is effectively managed will sustainable benefits for patients and for staff be realised. As a consequence it is helpful to think through your approach to helping people cope with change.

There are many different models of change management that can be used. In Chapter Eight I described William Bridges' 'transitions model' which provides a good insight in to how people cope individually with the process of change. Whatever model is adopted it is important that the lean leader should have a game plan. Create an exciting vision of where you want to be. Seek out allies, secure early wins on issues that matter and above all try to make it fun!

Thedacare have concluded that they need to develop 'standard work' for the change management process. They have done this by adopting the ideas of a number of leading thinkers on change management including John Kotter and William Bridges. The Thedacare Change Model is set out diagrammatically on the opposite page.

As well as having a systematic approach to change management, it is important to develop empathy with how it feels to 'be changed'. Our Simpler sensei have taught us an effective exercise to use in training sessions for staff who are new to the lean process. The participants in the training session are asked to take out of their pockets or purses their wallet or money folder. This sounds a bit like the kind of trick a magician might pull in a cabaret lounge and there are usually nervous giggles and sideways glances all around the room. The trainer then asks everyone to hold their wallet or purse in the air with one hand. The sense of nervous tension increases. The trainer then says 'okay, what we are going to do in a minute is take everything out of your wallet or purse, the cash, the photographs, the personal items, then we are going to mix them all up in a heap on the middle of your tables and teach you a lean process for sorting everything back in to your own wallet'. It's at this point that the participants begin to wish they had never volunteered for this particular programme! The trainer quickly moves on to say that he or she is only joking and everyone can put their wallets and purses away. They then asked 'so how did that feel?'. Of course the answer is 'pretty damned uncomfortable'.

The participants in the training session are asked to remember that feeling and hold on to it any time they visit a part of the hospital in which they are doing lean work. Asking staff to describe their work processes and openly share problems is akin to emptying all the personal contents out of your wallet and spreading it out on the table. This

Figure 32: Thedacare Change Model – Draft 2

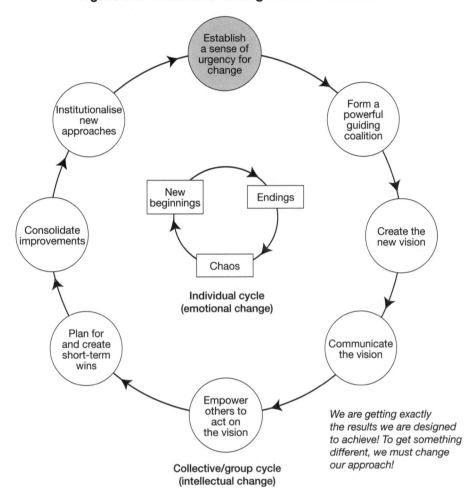

Sources: 'Leading change' (John Kotter; 'Managing transitions' (William Bridges); 'Making sense of change management' (Cameron & Green)

exercise never fails to resonate and to create a healthy degree of respect for others feelings. 'Don't forget we are asking people to open up their wallets here' is a phrase often heard during lean events.

Drawing strengths from others and from within yourself

The one certain thing about your lean transformation is that not everything will proceed smoothly. As a military friend of mine is fond of saying 'no plan survives first contact with the enemy'. There will be inevitable opposition and setbacks. Some people may be unhappy at the whole idea of trying to apply a foreign manufacturing concept to something as important as caring for patients. Others will be resistant to the idea of changing long established working practices or affronted at the suggestion that the service being delivered is less than perfect. It would be a miracle if all your lean improvement efforts delivered exactly what you had intended.

Whether you are running a small department or a large hospital you will be attempting your lean healthcare transformation at the same time as continuing to treat patients and meet the expectations of your bosses, funders and regulators. If your budget is overspent and your waiting times getting worse, no one will be impressed by the excuse 'but we were distracted by carrying out our lean transformation'. Even the best run healthcare organisations suffer from mishaps which can be high profile and damaging to the patients affected, to the morale of staff and to the reputation of the organisation. During the dark times you may wonder why you ever started down this road.

Of course as the leader, you're the person responsible for pulling everybody through the difficult patches. Even when you are feeling depressed or lacking in confidence, you need to be able to appear to be just the opposite. This takes strength of character and strength of will. There may be some super-human types who can do this all by themselves. I don't know about you but I am certainly not one of them. When things get really tough then the importance of a close knit, supportive team becomes readily apparent. Having a group of like-minded colleagues who know each other well, who share the same values and who have signed up to the same vision can make all the difference in times of intense pressure.

Such teams don't just happen by accident, it's the job of leaders to build and nurture them. The payments that you make in to the emotional bank with your team are repaid many fold in the support that they provide at times of crisis. Being able to achieve this depends not just on understanding the personalities and motivations of the different members of your team, it also demands that you know yourself. Having the insight to be aware of your own strengths and weaknesses and how these impact on other people is essential. Being clear about your own values, what's important to you in your life and your career, can help to guide you when you begin to doubt whether or not you are doing the right thing.

Delivering a lean transformation in healthcare or anywhere else takes courage, patience and persistence often over many years. It's unlikely to win you many promotions or plaudits. It may be worth reflecting on some excellent advice I was given by a respected friend at a turning point in my career 'You've got to decide', he said, 'Do you want to do something or just be somebody. Being somebody is easy, it's just about getting a fancy job title. To do something you've got to see things through the difficult times and build something that's going to last'.

So, my personal reflections on the first steps on our lean journey have identified lots of pitfalls to avoid, mistakes that shouldn't be repeated and lessons that we'd do well to learn carefully. The strongest of all my reflections is how immensely enjoyable, satisfying and uplifting the task can be. The last three years have been far and away the most stimulating period of my career and that of which I am the most proud. That's not to say that the results are as yet outstanding, although some of the early signs are certainly promising. But the speed of learning has been exhilarating and the glimpse of the potential that is there creates a sense of eager impatience.

Most satisfying of all has been seeing those patients who have benefited from the improvements that have been made. The improvements in our trauma service can be reduced to dry statistics, a 50% reduction in mortality rates. But if you imagine a London double-decker bus filled with your close friends and relatives, that's how many lives have been saved through the lean redesign of our trauma service in a two year period. Such a thought brings home the importance and potential of what we are doing.

It's not only those who receive this service that have benefited. I can think of countless examples of staff who were tired and disillusioned two years ago and who felt victims of problems they couldn't control. Those same staff today have visibly grown and developed in stature. They are energised by what they have done, proud of their achievements and excited by the prospect of the improvements to come. Can lean work in healthcare? Most certainly it can. Will it be a quick or easy journey? I am afraid not. Is the prize worth the effort? Without a shadow of a doubt.

References
1. Rogers, E. (1995) *The Diffusion of Innovations*, New York: The Free Press.
2. Collins, J. (2001) *Good to Great*, London: Random House.

Further reading

The following are books and articles that have helped to inspire and guide me as I have embarked on my own lean journey. Lots more information can be found via the internet. A good place to start is the Lean Enterprise Academy's website at www.lean.org.uk.

The application of lean in the NHS is explored on the NHS National Institute for Innovation and Improvement's website at www.institute.nhs.uk/qualityandvalue/lean

Balle, M. (2005) *The Goldmine: a novel of lean turnaround*, Cambridge MA: Lean Enterprise Institute.

Bridges, W. (2003) *Managing Transitions*, Cambridge MA: Perseus Books.

Collins, J. (2001) *Good to Great*, Ramdon House, London

Dennis, P. (2005) *Andy and Me: crisis and transformation on the lean journey*, New York: Productivity Press.

Dennis, P. (2006) *Getting the right things done: a leaders guide to planning and execution*, Cambridge MA: Lean Enterprise Institute.

Downey, M. (2003) *Effective Coaching*, Mason, OH: Tevere.

Drew, J., McCallum, B. & Roggerhofer, S. (2004) *Journey to Lean: making operational change stick*, New York: Palgrave MacMillan.

Henderson, B. & Larco, J. (2003) *Lean Transformation: how to change your business into a lean enterprise*, Richmond, VA: The Oaklea Press.

Hino, S. (2006) *Inside the mind of Toyota: Management principles for enduring growth*, New York: Productivity Press.

Institute of Healthcare Improvement (2005) *Going Lean in Healthcare*, Cambridge, MA: IHI.

Jones, D. & Mitchell, A. (2006) *Lean thinking for the NHS*, London: NHS Confederation.

Lawrence, D. (2002) *From Chaos to Care*, Cambridge MA: Perseus Books.

Liker, J. (2004) *The Toyota Way: 14 management principles from the world's greatest manufacturer*, McGraw Hill, New York

Liker, J. & Meier, D. (2006) *The Toyota Way Fieldbook: a practical guide for implementing Toyota's 4Ps*, New York: McGraw Hill.

Locock, L. (2001) *Maps and Journeys: redesign in the NHS*, Birmingham: Health Services Management Centre.

Mango, P. & Shepin, L. (2001) Hospitals get serious about operations, *The McKinsey Quarterly*, number 2, pp 74–85.

Mann, D. (2005) *Creating a Lean Culture: tools to sustain lean conversions*, New York: Productivity Press.

Neiman, R. (2004) *Execution Plain and Simple*, New York: McGraw Hill.

Ohno, T. (1988) *Toyota Production System: Beyond large scale production*, New York: Productivity Press.

Porter, M.E. & Teisberg, E.O. (2006) *Redefining Healthcare: creating value-based competition on results*, Boston, MA: Harvard Business School Press.

Spear, S. (2004) Learning to Lead at Toyota, *Harvard Business Review*, May, pp 78–106.

Spear, S. (2005) Fixing healthcare from the inside today, *Harvard Business Review*, September.

Smalley, A. (2005) *TPS vs Lean and the Law of unintended consequences*, www.superfactory.com/articles

Taninecz, G. (2005) *Massachusetts General Looks to lean*, www.superfactory.com/articles

Weber, D. (2006) Toyota-style management drives Virginia Mason, *The Physician Executive*, January/February, pp 12–17.

Womack, J., Jones, D. & Roos, D. (1990) *The machine that changed the world*, New York: Free Press.

Womack, J. & Jones, D. (2003) *Lean thinking: banish waste and create wealth in your corporation*, New York: Free Press.

Womack, J. & Jones, D. (2005) *Lean Solutions: how companies and customers can create value and wealth together*, London: Simon and Schuster.

Young, T., Braisford, S., Connell, C., Davies, R., Harper, P. & Klein, J. (2004) Using industrial processes to improve patient care, *BMJ*, Volume 328, January, pp 162–164.